Careers with a Science Degree

Over 100 job ideas to inspire you

Jenny Barron and Helen Evans

Student Helpbook Series

Lifetime
Publishing

Careers with a Science Degree - Over 100 job ideas to inspire you

Fifth edition

Published by Lifetime Publishing, Mill House, Stallard Street, Trowbridge BA14 8HH

© Nord Anglia Lifetime Development South West Ltd, 2010

ISBN 978-1-904979-39-5

Cover design by Arthouse Creative

Illustrations by Royston Robertson

Printed in the EU by SS Media Ltd

Contents

Career profiles

About the authors

Jenny Barron and Helen Evans are part of the in-house author team at Lifetime Publishing. They contribute to the widely used CLIPS careers information system and have authored a range of other student helpbooks and careers resources. Prior to turning to careers work, Helen, as a science graduate, worked in research in freshwater biology.

Acknowledgements

The figures quoted in Chapter five are reproduced with permission from 'What Do Graduates Do? 2009', produced by the Higher Education Careers Services Unit (HECSU) and the Association of Graduate Careers Advisory Services (AGCAS). Source of raw data: HESA Destination of Leavers from Higher Education 2007/8.

Thanks are due to Dr Nizar Ben Ayed, Christopher Curd, Dr Lionel Hill, Vicki Hodges, Dr Louissa Marsh and Dr Sarah Polack who are currently pursuing scientific careers and have kindly agreed to describe their experiences within this book.

Thanks also to Neil Harris for his contribution to the previous edition.

Section 1
Thinking about your future

Chapter one

Why science?

This chapter is aimed at everyone who is considering a science-based degree or career, but still feels a bit undecided about it. The chapter covers:

- the fascination and value of science
- where science can take you
- who science is for - i.e. everyone - that includes you, girls!

Science is fascinating

Science is about concepts and ideas. It engages our curiosity about why our world is as it is and how things work. Solving scientific problems develops our ingenuity. No matter how much we discover about our world there is always much more to be discovered. Scientific investigation never ends.

Scientific understanding is of great value to individuals and to society as a whole, in many areas of modern life. Whether your interest lies in researching groundbreaking scientific ideas or developing new products, whether it takes the form of a concern for the environment or world health, or is simply a natural curiosity about what things are made of and how they work, science can offer you a career that will challenge you, provide huge job satisfaction and involve you in a career that can provide benefits to us all.

Science offers the chance to be involved in matters that are at the forefront of our understanding. The past few years have seen cloning, the mapping of the human genome, landings on Mars, energy from wind and wave power and other remarkable advances. Future scientific developments will include:

- greater understanding of the nature of dark matter

- nanoscience/nanotechnology - the development of products the size of a nanometre (a millionth of a millimetre), resulting in even further miniaturisation of electrical circuits

- advances in our understanding of the impact of climate change - and how to deal with it

- greater applications of stem cell research, which could lead to huge advances in the treatment of certain medical conditions

- more genetic mapping in relation to human diseases, leading to the development of improved diagnostic techniques and treatment

- the further development of biometrics, such as face recognition systems

- the utilisation of fusion energy and further development of other sources of clean, safe alternatives to carbon-based fuels.

By choosing science you could be involved in any of these or other areas - either in pure research or in applying our scientific knowledge to develop new and improved products and services.

Where science can take you

Into science-related careers

Section 2 of this book shows the wide range of science-related careers available. And, contrary to popular perceptions of a scientist, see how few actually involve working in a laboratory! There is such a variety of careers on offer, a science degree can take you from the arctic to the tropics, or from working on a space programme to being a patent agent.

However, whatever scientific field you choose to work in, collaboration and communication are watchwords. Scientists work very much as a team – with other scientists and, in many career areas, with non-science colleagues. They need to be able to communicate with colleagues, customers and clients, as well as with the general public and decision makers, such as politicians. Scientists don't work in isolation! Many scientists find great satisfaction in the contact they have with other scientists, working together to solve problems and push back the scientific frontiers!

One of the particular features of a scientific career is the international dimension it can offer. Scientific ideas and applications are not limited by national boundaries, or by local custom and practice. Many UK-based research scientists work on European-wide or international projects, collaborating with their fellow scientists abroad on a regular basis, through electronic means and, for some, through spending time abroad. Botanists working on an international plant mapping project, and physicists working on an international project to develop new energy sources are just a couple of examples. Some scientists choose to spend longer periods working abroad, perhaps for several years.

Into non-scientific careers

There is a very close association in many people's minds between science the subject and science the career. However, having a science degree does not automatically mean you are committing yourself to a career in science. There are **many** other areas where you can make use of the skills gained through a science degree. Many of these are described in Section 3.

Who is science for?

The answer is, of course, that science is for everybody – whatever your background or gender. The health of the future economy of the UK depends on having enough people with the necessary scientific and technical expertise. There has been concern over recent years about getting enough people to choose to study science at degree level and then to enter it as a career. And of those that do take up a science degree and career, females are under-represented in many areas.

Initiatives to encourage you into science

Whatever your gender, if you have yet to make your degree choice, there are a number of initiatives running to encourage students to take science, technology, engineering and maths (STEM) subjects beyond GCSE, and pursue careers in those fields. Schemes are run nationwide, and annually involve thousands of students.

Initiatives run by EDT (see www.etrust.org.uk) include:

- Headstart – residential STEM experience courses at universities, for 16- to 17-year-olds

- Engineering Education Scheme – real-life, six-month STEM projects for those aged 16 and 17

- The Year in Industry – career development work placements for students on a gap year prior to university, and for undergraduates.

The **Smallpeice Trust** also offers residential taster courses on various aspects of engineering. See www.smallpeicetrust.org.uk for more details.

Physics has been a particular subject of concern. Even students who achieve really high grades at GCSE seem to shy away from the subject: recent research (undertaken by Cambridge Assessment) has found that even students who get the highest grades at GCSE science (A* or A) are more likely to take A level chemistry or biology than physics. (And of those that do take physics at A level, you won't be surprised to learn that the majority are male.)

At degree level, there is also a difference between subjects. For example, in 2007/08, there were over twice as many full-time undergraduate students studying biological studies subjects than there were taking physical science subjects (including chemistry).

So, if you have an interest in science, and particularly in physics and chemistry, why not pursue it and make a career of it?

Where are you, girls!

When you look at the ratios of males and females taking single subject degrees in biology, physics and chemistry, there are marked differences. Let's look at the figures for the academic year of 2007/08. While females were in the majority in biology (around 14,000 females compared to over 9,000 males), they were woefully under-represented in physics - there were nearly four times as many males taking physics as females.

In chemistry too, males also outnumbered females, by around 9,000 to around 6,500 respectively. (N.B. All these figures include both full- and part-time undergraduate and postgraduate students.)

Leading female scientists are also thin on the ground. Today, one of the most well-known female scientists in the UK is the neuroscientist Baroness Susan Greenfield, the first woman to become Director of the Royal Institution of Great Britain. However, you may be hard pushed to name any more! Not enough women are choosing careers in science, engineering and construction – despite there being skill shortages in these fields. So, if you are a female reading this, why not help to change things?

There is support and encouragement. **WISE – Women into Science, Engineering and Construction** (www.wisecampaign.org.uk) is a national campaign that collaborates with industry and education to encourage young women to value and pursue STEM or construction-related courses in school or college, and to move into related careers. The **Women's Engineering Society (WES)** (www.wes.org.uk) is a supportive membership organisation for female engineers and students.

So, give it a go girls!

Only you can choose

Information about careers comes to you from many different sources and you have been absorbing it ever since you were young. Now you are able to be more discriminating and can look more critically at the information you pick up.

Things change, especially in the field of science. New opportunities may arise which do not yet exist. New discoveries and influences, both economic and social, will affect the prospects for scientists in the future.

You will change too. You will develop new skills and interests. You may find you become much better than you thought at some things that you now find difficult. You could find you are brilliant at something you have not even tried yet! Your values may change. You might find, for example, that you become passionately involved in some environmental or health issue. Your career will develop according to your changing interests.

But although none of us can predict the future, it's not an excuse for doing nothing now, and drifting into a course or career, in the hope things will all turn out right in the end. It's your life, and you are the best person to have control of it. Take time to look at all the career options presented in this book and get researching. You never know where it may lead you!

Chapter two

Preparing for higher education

This chapter covers:

- choosing your level 3 subjects and courses – for those who have yet to choose their A level or equivalent courses

- choosing your higher education (HE) course – for those who have yet to choose their degree (or other course beyond level 3). This includes information about the different types of HE courses available to you and some subject ideas related to science for you to consider.

- the value of studying for a science degree.

Choosing your level 3 subjects and courses

For most students, A levels remain the typical route into higher education, but there are an increasing number of alternative pathways. The main science-related qualifications at advanced level (known as level 3) are outlined below.

A levels/Applied A levels

The main science subjects to consider are **chemistry, physics** and **biology**. To that list must be added **mathematics** – an extremely important subject if aiming at a science degree. Study of chemistry, physics and biology at A level will give you the opportunity to build on the subject knowledge you have gained at GCSE level. Good grades at GCSE science, or in the individual science subjects, will be needed.

There are also various other science-related AS/A levels that you could consider. However, not all schools and colleges offer all of these. As you may be less familiar with these subjects, they are described briefly below.

- **Applied science** offers the opportunity to study in a practical way while you learn about science in the workplace. It can be studied as a single-award qualification or a double-award A level (equivalent to two A levels).

- **Applied engineering** is another applied A level, available as a single-award qualification.

- **Environmental studies** offers the chance to gain a broad understanding of the environment and to learn about the social, economic and political aspects of environmental management. It has some topics in common with biology and geography. If combined with biology, you should check that the two subjects would be counted separately for entry to HE courses.

- **Design and technology** has specialist pathways in systems and control; product design; and food technology.

- **Human biology** may appeal to you if you have a particular interest in the human body, but less interest in continuing your studies of biology in a wider sense.

- **Science in society** helps you to develop the knowledge and skills that are needed to understand how science works and to analyse contemporary issues. It is mainly aimed at those taking non-science A levels, but could be considered by students taking science A levels who want to look at their specialist studies in a wider context.

If you are thinking about taking any of the above, it is very important that you **check entry requirements** to any HE courses that you are considering. **Many science degree courses require one or more subjects from physics, chemistry, biology or maths**, so you will need to consider your A level subject combinations carefully. You don't want to narrow down your options for HE courses, unless you are absolutely sure what you are ruling out!

Advanced Diplomas

Diploma qualifications, available in England, combine theoretical study with applied and practical learning about a broad area of work. Advanced Diplomas that may be of interest to someone who enjoys science include engineering, manufacturing and product design, and environmental and land-based studies.

BTEC National qualifications

BTEC courses also allow you to learn about an area of work. There is a range of BTEC National qualifications in applied science, including applied biology, applied chemistry and forensic science. (N.B. By the end of 2010, these qualifications will be retitled as level 3 qualifications to fit into the new Qualifications and Credit Framework.)

Job-related qualifications

Qualifications that you gain when training in the workplace can lead to entry to certain HE courses related to that field of work. You could gain, for example, an NVQ at level 3, or equivalent, through taking an Advanced Apprenticeship.

Access courses

Access courses in science offer a route into HE, aimed particularly at those who have had some time away from education and do not hold the required HE entry qualifications.

Choosing your subjects/course combinations

Entry to higher education

Entry requirements for **degree courses** are normally a minimum of either two A levels, a double-award applied A level, a BTEC National qualification, an Advanced Diploma or an equivalent qualification. You will also need supporting GCSEs, or equivalent. Often entry requirements are described in UCAS Tariff points. The Tariff is explained on the UCAS website and in *Big Guide*, published by UCAS. Many courses require more than the minimum stated above, and/or demand particular subjects. For example, entry requirements for a degree course may state that A level maths is essential, or that you need to hold either biology or chemistry at A level. For some courses, BTEC National qualifications are only acceptable in combination with an A level in a particular subject. However, there are often great variations between HE institutions in entry requirements for the same degree subject. So it's worth doing your research!

Mix and match

One of the advantages of the range of level 3 qualifications on offer is that you can mix and match academic and vocational subjects. For example it can be possible to combine a BTEC National qualification with an A level, or you could take an A level with an Advanced Diploma. Many people also choose a mixture of arts and sciences at A level, by studying a humanities or creative subject alongside science subjects. This can give you a more varied programme and will allow you insights into a different subject area. However, you need to be sure you are still taking enough science subjects to keep your HE options open.

How many sciences?

If you are going down the A level route, taking biology, chemistry, physics and maths would keep open the very widest choice of science degree courses! However, you may not want to study all these subjects, and it is not necessary. On the other hand, taking only one science subject to the full A level is not advisable, if you want to go on to science at HE. So, think about your interests and abilities, and take advice from your teachers, and again, check HE entry requirements.

Try to maintain your maths base

Because mathematics is such an essential tool for sciences it is important to try to take it as far as you can. If you are not sure whether you are capable of taking a full maths A level, consider taking it to AS level. Discuss the options with your teachers. If you are taking a science-based, vocationally-related qualification (such as a BTEC or an A level in an applied subject), to keep as many HE options open as possible, you should try to enhance your qualifications with as much extra mathematics as you can.

Above all, when deciding on your subject combinations, you need to check that the combination of subjects and courses you finally choose are acceptable for entry to any degree or other HE course you may want to move on to.

So, research all the courses available in your area – not only in your school, if it has a sixth form, but also at local further education and sixth form colleges. You will be studying in much more depth than you have previously, so it makes sense to look at course content carefully, check whether the assessment methods would suit you and look at where the course could lead you. There is a lot to weigh up, but take advice from teachers and careers/personal advisers.

Choosing your higher education course

This section of the chapter is for all who are exploring their options for study at higher education (HE) level.

All too many students drop out of HE because of a change of heart or because the course they chose did not meet their expectations, so do not rush into any decisions. Besides deciding which **subject** or subjects you are interested in studying, you will be faced with choices about the **type of course** to take.

Different types of course

The following is a brief overview of all the different levels and types of HE courses. As you will see, the HE qualifications available other than degrees are mainly offered in vocational (work-related) subjects, and take two years' full-time study.

First degrees

Degree courses (sometimes referred to as first degrees to differentiate them from higher or postgraduate degrees) are offered in a huge range of academic and vocational subjects. Degrees usually require three or four years of full-time study. Traditionally, first degrees are offered as single honours (study of a single subject) or joint or combined honours (two or more subjects studied). Modular programmes, where students gradually build up their degree by taking individual units of study, offer the most flexibility.

For general information about entry qualifications for degree courses, look at the earlier section in this chapter, under 'Choosing your level 3 subjects and courses'.

Enhanced courses: some single-science degrees, particularly physics and chemistry, are enhanced by the addition of an extra year. These go by the title MSci, MPhys and MChem. Enhanced degrees give students a deeper appreciation of their subject than the shorter courses, and are aimed at those who want to take their studies to a high level, in preparation for postgraduate study and/or a professional career as a scientist.

Foundation year courses: some science degrees incorporate an initial foundation year – sometimes referred to as year 0. Science foundation years are aimed at students without the usual entry requirements, such as those with non-science A levels. The year will bring the student's science knowledge up to a level where they can progress onto the first year of the degree.

Foundation degrees

Not to be confused with foundation years, as described above, foundation degrees usually offer a mix of work-related skills and academic study. They are mainly offered in vocationally-related subjects, such as pharmaceutical science and applied biology. They take two years, full time, and are also available through part-time or distance-learning routes – aimed at those in relevant employment.

There are no nationally-set entry requirements. Each institution sets its own entry criteria. The most important requirement is that you are capable of studying at HE level. Some institutions will ask for evidence of this, which could be previous study at A level or equivalent, an NVQ level 3, an Advanced Apprenticeship or completion of relevant work experience.

Higher National Diplomas (HNDs)

HNDs are also vocationally-related qualifications lasting two years, full time. They combine theory and practice, and prepare students for employment at technician, supervisory and management level.

Higher National Certificates (HNCs) are generally studied for on a part-time basis over two years, for people in relevant employment. However there are a few full-time HNCs available, which take a year to complete.

Entry requirements to Higher National courses are flexible: admissions tutors may require one A level pass (often with a second subject studied to A level), a BTEC National qualification or possibly an NVQ level 3. If you have a vocational qualification it should be in a related subject area.

Diplomas of Higher Education (DipHEs)

A DipHE is a qualification in its own right, normally awarded after completing the equivalent of two years of degree-level study. There are relatively few DipHE courses. While most are vocational, there are some in non-vocational subjects. Entry requirements are often the same as for degree courses.

Other questions to ask yourself

- **Are you interested in a full-time, part-time or distance learning course?** You might not have considered the idea of studying for HE on a part-time basis before. But many people do, and many earn while they learn. If the HE course is relevant to your job, your employer may contribute to course fees and allow you time off work to attend college or university. Others opt for the distance-learning option, such as through the Open University. For this approach, you need to be confident that you have the motivation to study independently.

- **Would you like to spend time getting work experience as part of your studies?** Some courses may offer a short work placement during the course. Alternatively, sandwich courses, as they are called, incorporate a longer period of work experience with an employer, generally lasting a year. If taking a degree, this usually takes place after the second year of study. Gaining such experience can prove beneficial when applying for jobs after your degree. See Chapter three for more information about the value of gaining work experience while you are studying.

- **Might it be helpful to gain some relevant work experience prior to your higher education studies?** This could prove beneficial when looking for employment after your HE course, and, while on your course, help you to put your learning into context. The Year in Industry (YINI) programme offers work placements, including in science and engineering, for students considering a gap year. See www.yini.org.uk for more information.

- **Could you find an employer that might sponsor you while on your course?** Sponsorship funding is difficult to find, but some students on courses related to engineering, science and technology are sponsored by an employer. Contact employers of interest to you, and ask HE course admissions tutors about any companies that sponsor students on their courses.

- **Would you like to study in another country as part of your course?** A number of science-related degrees offer a period in another country as part of the course, either studying at a university or, possibly, working in industry. Chapter five discusses the international dimension of science-related careers; studying abroad may give you a head-start if this aspect of the work particularly appeals to you.

- **Are you considering progression from one level of course to another?** It is often possible to move from an HND to a degree course in a similar subject, or top up a foundation degree to a full honours degree, with an extra year of study.

- **Are you interested in a subject you haven't studied before, but slightly unsure about taking it at HE level?** Most courses require you to study other related subjects at least for the first year, before you specialise in a particular subject. This gives you a chance to try out new subjects before narrowing down.

What to study

One big advantage of taking science subjects at level 3 is that you will have a huge range of HE courses open to you. The downside is that this choice can be quite bewildering. Broadly speaking, science courses fall into one of the following categories.

Pure science: this is the study of the basic principles of science. At degree level, you can continue with physics, chemistry and biology, or choose new subjects or ones you may have studied as part of an A level course, such as biochemistry, geology, oceanography, genetics, ecology or physiology.

Courses can be taken as single subjects or combined with other related subjects, such as physics with astrophysics, biology and computer science, chemistry with pharmacology. There are also combinations with unrelated subjects, like physics with management, biology and history, or chemistry and French.

Applied science: this is about making practical use of scientific principles and discoveries. Courses include food science, biotechnology, animal science, materials science and applied physics. Such courses often call on a variety of basic sciences in a multidisciplinary approach to a major topic.

Vocational: these are 'applied' courses designed to prepare you for a particular job. Examples are medicine, pharmacy, dietetics, biomedical science and dentistry.

What do you want to do after your HE course?

It is wise to look ahead and investigate the career options that will be open to you at the end of a course. Although some people begin HE with a definite career plan, they are in the minority. Most develop their skills, discover more about themselves and change their ideas as their studies progress. Lots change their minds about their original choice of course and about their career aims. Many are still undecided about their career direction even when they graduate.

Course ideas lists

Below you will find some **degree course** ideas, to act as a starting point for your research. Make a list of the subjects that interest you and find out more about them by viewing university websites and prospectuses. If there is a professional body that relates to the subject of interest to you, check whether they recognise or accredit any particular degree courses.

These course lists are only intended as an ideas generator – they are by no means fully comprehensive. New subject combinations and new courses with new titles appear every year. You must get the most up-to-date information before you make your choice.

There are four lists. First, depending on whether your particular interests lie in biology, chemistry or physics, look at list 1, 2 or 3 respectively, and then, whatever your interests, look at list 4.

1. Course ideas related to biological sciences

Anatomical science

Animal behaviour

Animal science

Applied biology

Bioarchaeology

Bioinformatics

Biological sciences

Biology

Cell biology

Conservation biology

Ecology

Environmental biology

Evolutionary biology

Forensic biology

Genetics

Human biology

Immunology

Marine/freshwater biology

Microbiology

Molecular biology

Nutrition

Physiology

Plant science/plant biology

Wildlife biology/conservation

Zoology

2. Course ideas related to chemistry

Applied chemistry

Chemical engineering

Chemistry

Chemistry with maths

Chemistry with nanotechnology

Chemistry with study abroad

Chemistry with a modern foreign language

Colour science

Cosmetic science

Environmental chemistry

Medicinal chemistry

Pharmaceutical science

Pharmacy

3. Course ideas related to physics

Acoustics

Applied physics

Astronomy

Astrophysics

Computational physics

Computer engineering

Engineering (aeronautical, biomedical, broadcast, civil, communications, electrical, electronics, mechanical, medical, production etc)

Geophysics

Mathematics and physics

Medical physics

Meteorology

Nuclear science

Particle physics

Physics

Physics and philosophy

Physics with a modern foreign language

Physics with nanotechnology

Physics with photonics

Physics with study abroad

Ship science

Sustainable energy

Theoretical physics

4. Other science-related courses that might interest you

Agriculture

Arboriculture

Archaeological science

Aquaculture

Audiology

Biochemistry

Biomedical engineering/Medical engineering

Biomedical science

Biotechnology

Chemical physics

Dentistry

Diagnostic radiography

Dietetics

Equine science

Engineering

Environmental health

Environmental science

Environmental conservation

Food science

Forensic science

Forestry

Geology/Earth sciences

Horticulture

Materials science

Medical science

Medicine

Metallurgy

Natural sciences

Nursing or Midwifery

Optometry

Orthoptics

Pharmacology

Physiotherapy

Podiatry

Sports science

Textile science

Veterinary science

Please note...

Beware of courses that look similar but are not. One, such as dietetics, may lead to a professional qualification while another, such as nutrition, may not. Do not assume that a degree course automatically leads to a career in a certain area. For example, a degree in forensic science does not automatically lead to a career as a forensic scientist!

Many of the above subjects can be studied in combination with non-science subjects, such as a modern language, business, history, English or law.

The value of studying for a science degree

There are many benefits of gaining degree-level qualifications. Whatever your subject – science or non-science – studying for a degree will:

- give you the opportunity to study a subject of interest to you up to a high level

- open up a wider range of career opportunities for you

- help you to develop a range of skills valued by employers

- increase your future earning potential

- provide you with the chance to make new friends from a range of backgrounds, and opportunities to develop new interests

- give you an experience you will always value.

A **science degree** has particular benefits.

A science degree gives you valuable skills

Besides up-to-date knowledge and technical ability, a science degree in particular will help you to develop analytical, teamworking, communication, research, critical-thinking and problem-solving skills.

A science degree opens doors

A science degree is a starting point for a lot of different career routes. As well as job areas where a science degree is essential or where scientific knowledge is an advantage, science graduates can enter the range of other career areas that are open to graduates of any discipline (described in Section 3).

A variety of career pathways will be open to you

There are those in research and academic jobs who will continue to work at the frontiers of science throughout their working lives. Alternatively, at a later stage in your life, it may be possible to move into other career areas. It is certainly much easier to move from science careers into non-science careers than the other way around!

Working it out

This chapter is just a starting point. There are many other things to be done before you can reach a decision about what to do in higher education. There are new ideas to consider, people to talk to and other sources of help and information to explore.

What help can you get?

- Talk to your science teachers, and teachers who advise on careers and university applications.

- Read more about the courses on offer through the UCAS website, in course prospectuses and university websites and in HE handbooks. Widen your general science knowledge through magazines such as New Scientist, the science pages of the quality newspapers, 'popular' science books, visits, lectures, open days and 'taster' courses at universities.

- Visit the websites of the major scientific institutions.

- Talk to your personal/careers adviser.

- Talk to someone who has completed a course that you are interested in, if you can.

- Investigate the websites of employers that may interest you.

- Try some work experience or holiday jobs.

- Discuss your thoughts with family and friends.

It is most important that you find out what the science courses that interest you are about, particularly if you have not studied the subjects at level 3. Don't just assume that you know – make sure you understand what is involved!

Consider the stage you are at now, and decide where you are in your career planning. If you need a professional qualification to get into the career of your choice, check that the courses you are considering are accredited by the relevant professional body. The more you find out, the more your interests will clarify and new ideas will grow. Make sure that you choose the course that will suit you best, because that will lead to success in your studies and the best chance of a career you will enjoy.

Chapter three

Preparing for your career

"Work experience?"

This chapter discusses ways in which you can improve your employability and start preparing for your career, while you are still an undergraduate. It covers:

- work experience
- supplementary skills you can develop alongside your degree
- boosting your CV through your extracurricular activities
- the careers services available to you.

To gain a degree in any subject is a notable achievement. However, on its own, a degree is unlikely to land you the job of your dreams. When it comes to finding work, you are going to find yourself competing with others who may be similarly, or even more-highly, qualified. So what can you do to give yourself an edge? The following describes ways in which you can prepare for your career while still a student, by adding value to your degree.

Work experience

Undertaking work experience while you are a student takes planning and motivation, but it offers significant benefits and will be looked upon favourably by future employers. The most beneficial option is to find work experience that is relevant to your course and future career ambitions, although any work undertaken as a sideline to your studies can still prove useful. In general, it allows you to:

- gain practical, hands-on experience that shows you can apply your academic studies to the 'real world'
- get an insight into the range of jobs available to you – what they involve and their potential progression routes
- 'try out' an employer to see if you like them
- start building a network of contacts
- develop an understanding of the 'world of work', which will eventually help you to settle into a permanent role more easily
- potentially gain a future referee, to use when applying for jobs after your degree
- possibly earn some money!

Don't forget – work experience also lets an employer 'try you out' to see if they like you! Employers are increasingly using work experience placements as an extended 'interview' for places on their graduate training schemes or for other permanent roles further down the line.

Degrees with built-in work experience

If you have yet to select your degree course, you could think about choosing one that incorporates work experience. **Sandwich courses** typically last four years and combine full-time study with one or more industrial placements, i.e. supervised, practical experience and training with an employer. Look into how closely connected your higher education (HE) institution is with key employers in the industry and how much help you will receive in finding placements. Note also that **foundation degrees** and **HNDs** offer a high level of work-based learning, and can be 'topped up' to a full degree with further study.

Internships

Also known as summer placements, vacation schemes, work experience and so on, **undergraduate internships** offer a fixed period of employment during your vacation. They are usually offered to students in their penultimate or final year of studies.

If it's not long until you graduate, or you have just done so, a **graduate internship** may be worth considering. As for other types of work experience, they can help make you more employable, or they may offer a stop-gap if you are struggling to find a permanent position.

The number of internships is on the increase. Major employers often see them as a means of selecting the best candidates for permanent positions on their graduate training schemes. Others may offer them with a specific short-term project in mind. In recent times, the Government has also been encouraging employers to take on graduate interns as a means of addressing unemployment among young people. Not all internships offer paid employment however; in some cases you will only be paid expenses.

Competition for places can be fierce, so it is worth doing your research well in advance to find out what's available and exactly when and how you need to apply. Employers usually follow a formal application process, expecting you to apply in writing, attend an interview and, possibly, undertake tests at an assessment centre. They may also set criteria regarding your grades; for example, only accepting candidates who have achieved, or are predicted, at least a 2:2.

Most HE institutions provide support to students looking for internships. Ask at your institution's careers service or placement office, or look for information in the library. The *Student Guide to Work Experience* may be available from such sources; alternatively it is available to purchase for a small charge from the National Council for Work Experience. See www.work-experience.org for further details, and for a list of companies that have been accredited for the quality of their work experience placements.

Many major employers run internship programmes, including P&G, GSK, Centrica, BP, Cancer Research and so on. However, don't overlook the opportunities available with smaller employers. For example, the *Shell Step* programme matches undergraduates to small and medium-sized companies and community organisations for paid, project-based work placements. See www.shellstep.org.uk for full details.

There are various organisations that can help students from under-represented groups find internships. For example, EmployAbility works primarily with disabled students, see www.employ-ability.org.uk. Some employers also target under-represented groups. The Civil Service is an example of such an employer; it offers *Summer Diversity Internship Programmes* aimed at disabled students and students from black and ethnic minority backgrounds. For more information, visit www.civilservice.gov.uk/summerdiversity.

You can search online for internships with a wide range of employers via the Prospects website at www.prospects.ac.uk/workexperience.

N.B. At the time of writing the Department for Business, Innovation and Skills is running the *Graduate Talent Pool* scheme. This is an online vacancy service, which allows recent graduates to search and apply for internships. It is not yet known whether this will be an ongoing scheme; it is currently limited to applicants who graduated in 2008 or 2009. See www.direct.gov.uk/graduatetalentpool for further details.

Supplementary skills

Most degree courses will help you develop a range of transferable skills, such as teamwork, time management and so on. While employers certainly value these 'soft' skills, they may also look for ability in other, more practical areas, such as languages and ICT.

You are likely to have the opportunity to develop such skills at your HE institution through:

- course modules that can be taken alongside your main studies

- evening classes, often at a discount price

- self-study; for example, through access to a language or IT centre and its resources.

Language skills are obviously useful if you want to work or study abroad, but also if you want to work in the UK for an organisation with international connections. Most HE institutions offer a wide range of modern foreign languages; think about which languages could be of most benefit to your situation. You can find out about science degrees that incorporate language skills and international placements in Chapter five.

You are also likely to be able to develop your **ICT skills**, not only in the specific technologies that relate to your field of study, but also in generic applications, such as wordprocessing, spreadsheet, database, presentation, image manipulation and web-related packages.

As an induction to most degree courses, you are likely to be offered help in developing your **research and information skills**. This is likely to include how to use the web effectively, perform literature searches and make full use of library resources. Such skills are critical to achieving a degree, but also have many applications in the workplace.

You may be surprised at what else may be on offer - short courses to develop your **enterprise skills, get published,** or learn how to **touch type** or **drive**; sessions with **guest speakers** and much more! Contact your student support service for further information.

Extracurricular activities

The higher education experience isn't just about studying! There are many clubs and societies you can join at most institutions, which can offer a welcome break from academia. While these offer a chance to indulge your passions, or develop new ones, they can also enhance your CV in the eyes of a potential employer.

Think of all the transferable skills you can gain from being a member of a sports team, debating society, drama club, music group, college radio station, or student union entertainment team! Potential employers will be able to use this as evidence that you are team player, or even a natural leader, and that you are skilled at organisation, negotiation and promotion, for example. In the absence of work experience, being able to demonstrate these skills from other areas of your life will be vital. Showing that you have a healthy work-life balance may also be important.

Other options may include joining an Armed Forces university unit or undertaking voluntary work, the Duke of Edinburgh Award programme, Young Enterprise Graduate Programme or other scheme that shows evidence of personal development.

Careers services

HE institutions are very keen to see their students find suitable employment after graduation, so tend to offer a great deal of support in this respect. They may offer a careers service not only to current students, but also to those that have already graduated, although possibly for a limited amount of time only.

Typical support includes one-to-one guidance sessions, workshops, careers events and access to a variety of resources. You can use these services to find out about your options, clarify you career aspirations, practise applications and interviews, take aptitude tests, research employers and vacancies, investigate postgraduate study options or get advice about starting your own business.

Careers fairs and the 'milk round'

Careers fairs, organised by HE institutions, tend to take place in autumn and spring terms and give you the opportunity to meet with potential employers. These may be major, national organisations as well as smaller, local employers. Such fairs may be seen by employers as a chance for them to 'sell' themselves to you!

The '**milk round**' is the informal name for the season of recruitment fairs that enable employers to start looking for potential graduate recruits. They may be organised by the HE institution careers service, or occasionally by independent organisations, that stage them in exhibition centres open to students from any HE institution. In general, recruitment fairs have been on the decline in recent times, partly because of the economic downturn, but also because of the rise in internet recruitment.

Employers that attend recruitment fairs tend to be the major, 'blue chip' companies that are looking to recruit to their formal graduate training schemes. Although you are very unlikely to be offered a position there and then, such encounters are still an important part of the recruitment process and should be approached as such! Research the employers that are of interest to you, take your CV, dress appropriately and be prepared to meet with managers and other key staff who will have some influence over your eventual recruitment. If possible, take contact details and follow up with employers after the event when you make your formal application.

Seize the day!

For many people, studying for a degree is a once in a lifetime opportunity and it's easy to look back on those exciting few years – and wonder where the time went! So it makes sense to exploit your time in higher education to the fullest. Gaining a degree is just part of the experience; if you can also start preparing for your future career in the ways described above, it will be time very well spent!

Chapter four

Postgraduate study options

This chapter covers:

- the benefits of postgraduate study
- the different types of postgraduate study
- funding postgraduate study
- postgraduate study abroad.

The benefits of postgraduate study

A postgraduate course can enable you to build on your degree by specialising in a topic of particular interest to you, developing new skills and in-depth knowledge as you do so. It may also offer an opportunity to improve your employability, particularly if you select a vocational course with a specific career goal in mind. There are many postgraduate courses in both scientific and non-scientific subjects leading to a wide range of different careers, which may suit you if you've taken a broad-based, non-vocational course at first degree level.

For some career areas, such as clinical science, environmental health, teaching and law, you'll need a professional qualification at postgraduate level. For others, a postgraduate qualification may not be essential but is likely to increase your job prospects, especially in highly competitive sectors. You'll need to research the career area you're interested in to find out how useful a postgraduate qualification may be.

You can find out more about entry requirements to different careers in Sections 2 and 3, which will give you an idea of some of the careers for which a postgraduate qualification is highly recommended. For example:

- to work in space science you usually need a relevant postgraduate qualification

- taking a relevant postgraduate course is likely to boost your career prospects in biotechnology work

- the majority of trainees in the newspaper industry are recruited after taking a full-time vocational course

- to work as a medical physicist, you need an accredited masters degree.

Types of postgraduate study

Postgraduate study is study that graduates undertake to gain a masters or doctoral degree, or a postgraduate diploma or certificate. Depending on the degree taken, study may be through a taught programme or through a research programme.

Taught programmes

Masters degrees have different titles according to the subject and method of study. Most masters degrees in scientific subjects lead to Master of Science (MSc), although some may lead to the award of a Master of Arts (MA). Programmes normally last 12 months, full time or two years, part time. They may be available as conversion courses to develop your skills in a new subject, such as business or IT, or be vocational courses that lead to a professional qualification.

Note that some undergraduate courses lead to the award of an MSci, MChem or MPhys. These are enhanced degrees, incorporating an additional year on top of a normal BSc course. The extra year enables students to undertake a research project or further study of a particular topic of interest. However, these are not equivalent to the postgraduate qualification of MSc.

Postgraduate diplomas/certificates – these courses are often vocational and include professional training, such as the Postgraduate Certificate in Education (PGCE) – one of the qualification routes to become a teacher, or a conversion course such as the Graduate Diploma in Law (GDL). They usually last nine months, full time or two years, part time. You may be able to upgrade your diploma to a masters degree.

If you enter work as a graduate, you may still go on to take further study. In many jobs you will be encouraged to take a relevant postgraduate course part time while working. This will form part of your ongoing professional development.

Research programmes

Master by Research (MRes) tends to be awarded in science and social science subjects and incorporates training in research techniques, as well as subject-specific modules. At least 60% of the course is based on an individual research project. The MRes typically takes around one year to complete and can lead on to a PhD programme.

Master of Philosophy (MPhil) usually signifies a masters degree obtained by research, in any subject. Research masters degrees involve the in-depth study of a defined subject over approximately two years. You are likely to receive training in research skills, and work independently to prepare a thesis. Many graduates begin a research masters degree with the intention of upgrading it to a PhD.

Doctor of Philosophy (PhD) is the highest level of academic qualification. The title of PhD is used across the full range of academic subjects. It involves at least three years of supervised research resulting in a thesis.

Around 20 UK universities now offer an 'integrated PhD', incorporating the traditional research requirements of a PhD with taught modules and training in key personal, research and professional skills. The 'NewRoutePhD' normally takes four years, full time and offers interim awards at diploma, certificate or masters level. Full details can be found at www.newroutephd.ac.uk.

Some science graduates choose to take a PhD purely because of their interest in the subject; others take one as a route into an academic career. A PhD is usually essential for entry into an academic career due to the competition for posts. There may be some opportunities to work towards a research degree in partnership with government or hospital laboratories, in research institutes or in industry.

Funding your postgraduate study

You'll need to think about how to fund your postgraduate study. Unfortunately, this is a problem for thousands of students because there simply isn't much funding available. One thing to note is that, in most cases, you will not be eligible for a student loan. You may need to work part time, or take time out to work before you begin postgraduate study, to raise funds for it.

You may be able to get funding through universities and colleges, from charitable organisations and trusts, or from employers and learned societies (such as the Royal Society). You could also apply to a bank for a Professional and Career Development Loan of up to £10,000, which you pay back after you've stopped studying. For more information visit www.direct.gov.uk/pcdl.

Funding for a wide range of research, including that undertaken by postgraduates, comes from the Research Councils, the seven public bodies with responsibility for investing in scientific innovations and their industrial applications. The Research Councils with most relevance to science graduates are the:

- Biotechnology and Biological Sciences Research Council (BBSRC)

- Engineering and Physical Sciences Research Council (EPSRC)

- Medical Research Council (MRC)

- Natural Environment Research Council (NERC)

- Science and Technology Facilities Council (STFC).

For links to all the Research Councils and for information about the collaborative work they do, visit the Research Councils UK's website, www.rcuk.ac.uk.

There are just a couple of exceptions to the standard funding arrangements for postgraduate courses. If you intend to train as a **teacher**, by studying for a PGCE, you will be eligible for a student loan. Students offered **NHS-funded places** on postgraduate programmes leading to professional registration have their tuition fees paid and can apply for an income-assessed NHS bursary.

The *Postgraduate Funding Guide* is published annually in September, by Prospects, and is a useful source of information about funding options. It may be available through your university careers service, or can be ordered online at www.prospects.ac.uk.

Postgraduate study abroad

Opportunities to study abroad are increasing, with literally thousands of universities overseas offering taught masters and research degrees. You may be attracted to the experience you'll gain spending time in a new country or by the opportunity to work with specialists in your field. Whatever your reasons for choosing postgraduate study abroad the range of courses is huge – from studying astrophysics in the USA to studying climate change in Denmark – and you'll certainly find one to suit your area of interest.

You will, however, need to research courses carefully. The range and quality of study available can differ widely from country to country. Course titles, content, entry requirements, length and funding can also vary. You'll need to check whether your existing qualifications are acceptable and think about how you are going to fit into another culture. Above all, studying abroad will involve a high level of personal commitment, as well as consideration of financial issues, so you'll need to think through all the options and practicalities carefully before you make a decision.

Chapter five

Science graduate destinations

While you are considering some of the career options available to you, it may be useful to reflect on how other science graduates before you have fared. You may also like to think about studying and working outside the UK – an exciting possibility for many scientists. To guide you, this chapter covers:

- graduate destinations
- starting salaries
- international opportunities
- profiles of six, real-life scientists, describing their careers.

Graduate destinations

While you will never know exactly what the future has in store for you, it can still be useful to look at what other people in similar situations have achieved as a way of assessing your own prospects. It can set your expectations at a realistic level – or it can spur you on to be one of the high-achievers who outperform the rest!

Remember, though, that you cannot control all the factors that may impact on your future career. For example, the UK was officially declared to be in recession at the start of 2009 and many jobs, vacancies, training opportunities, salaries and so on, were badly affected as a result. But, recessions – and boom times – come and go, so being in the right place at the right time is often down to luck, rather than judgement!

The following figures are from an annual survey and show the destination of students six months after they graduated in 2008. [The figures shown in the tables below and in the sections relating to employment destinations and starting salaries are reproduced with permission from 'What Do Graduates Do? 2009', produced by the Higher Education Careers Services Unit (HECSU) and the Association of Graduate Careers Advisory Services (AGCAS). Source of raw data: HESA Destination of Leavers from Higher Education 2007/8.]

	Scientific subjects – broad subject area					All subjects
	Biology	Chemistry	Physics	Environmental, Physical Geographical and Terrestrial Sciences	Sports Science	
No of graduates in 2008	4,260	2,505	1,950	3,015	6,955	276,930
No of survey respondents	3,495	2,055	1,650	2,545	5,665	220,065
Employed	51%	44%	38%	55%	61%	61%
Undertaking further study or training	24%	35%	36%	20%	17%	14%
Working and studing	7%	6%	9%	6%	8%	8%
Unemployed	9%	9%	9%	9%	6%	8%
Other	9%	7%	8%	10%	9%	9%

Note: percentages have been rounded up.

Figures from 'What Do Graduates Do? 2009' – see acknowledgements.

While considering these figures, remember that this group of graduates would have been caught up in the effects of the economic downturn, as mentioned previously. It is interesting to note that, for the class of 2008, 9% of science graduates were unemployed six months after graduating, a similar rate to most other graduates. Only sports science graduates bucked the trend, with just 6% unemployed six months after graduating.

Further study or training

From the previous table, it is also clear to see that graduates of biology, chemistry and physics are, on average, far more likely than other graduates to go on to further study or training. Over a third of chemistry and physics graduates and a quarter of biology graduates pursue this route, compared to one in seven of all graduates.

A further breakdown of the figures relating to students who were undertaking further study or training six months after graduating, show:

	Scientific subjects - broad subject area					All subjects
	Biology	Chemistry	Physics	Environmental, Physical Geographical and Terrestrial Sciences	Sports Science	
Studying in the UK for a higher degree	14.2%	27.3%	29.0%	12.3%	6.1%	6.6%
Studying in the UK for a teaching qualification	5.2%	4.2%	3.8%	5.4%	7.2%	2.5%
Undertaking other further study or training in the UK	4.5%	2.7%	2.6%	2.6%	3.1%	4.7%
Undertaking further study or training overseas	0.4%	0.4%	0.9%	0.1%	0.2%	0.2%
Total of all respondents	24.3%	34.6%	36.3%	20.4%	16.6%	14.0%

Figures from 'What Do Graduates Do? 2009' – see acknowledgements.

These figures show quite how common it is for physics and chemistry graduates to go on to study for higher degrees, i.e. masters degrees and doctorates. Also of note are the relatively high proportion of sports science graduates who go on to teacher training. And, although small in absolute terms, the proportion of physics graduates who go on to study or train overseas is almost five times the average of other students.

Employment

Of those graduates who were working six months after graduating, their typical jobs very much varied according to degree subject. Some of the major destinations are listed below.[1]

Of biology graduates in employment:

- 15% worked in **other professional, associate professional and technical occupations,** such as school science technicians

- 12% worked as **scientific research, analysis and development professionals.**

Of chemistry graduates in employment:

- 24% worked as **scientific research, analysis and development professionals**

- 17% worked in **other professional, associate professional and technical occupations,** such as laboratory technicians, trainee air traffic controllers, and assistant quantity surveyors

- 10% worked as **business and financial professionals and associate professionals,** such as internal auditors, economic analysts, and trainee accountants.

Of physics graduates in employment:

- 18% worked as **business and financial professionals and associate professionals,** such as finance analysts, actuaries and investment advisers

- 10% worked as **scientific research, analysis and development professionals**

- 10% worked as **information technology professionals**

---

[1] Figures from *'What Do Graduates Do? 2009'* – see acknowledgements.

- 8% worked in **other professional, associate professional and technical occupations**

- 7% worked as **engineering professionals**.

Of environmental, physical geographical and terrestrial sciences graduates in employment:

- 14% worked in **other professional, associate professional and technical occupations**, such as assistant transport consultants, town planning assistants, environmental health officers and surveyors

- 12% worked as **commercial, industrial and public sector managers**.

Of sports science graduates in employment:

- 24% worked as **arts, design, culture and sports professionals**, such as sports coaches, fitness instructors, sports officials and sports therapists

- 13% worked as **education professionals**, such as PE teachers and sports development officers

- 8% worked as **commercial, industrial and public sector managers**.

Starting salaries

Salaries for all students who graduated in 2008 and went into full-time work varied from an average of £14,543 for those who went into customer service occupations, to an average of £25,362 for those in health professions, such as doctors, dentists and pharmacists. Across all occupations, the average salary six months after graduating was **£19,677**. Those graduates who worked as science professionals had an average salary of £19,972.[1]

Whatever your starting salary, remember that as a graduate you have significant potential for progression over the course of your career. Your ultimate salary will depend on how committed you are to your continuing professional development (CPD), your performance, your ability at self-promotion and your ambition!

[1] Figures from *'What Do Graduates Do? 2009'* – see acknowledgements.

International opportunities for scientists

Scientists are part of a global community – undertaking international collaborations on major research projects, as well as exchanging ideas and sharing data through international conferences, visits and networks. There are, therefore, many opportunities for science graduates to work or study overseas at some stage in their careers.

British scientists have a distinct advantage in that English is the international language of science. However, although your scientific peers may understand written English and be able to conduct technical discussions, to work abroad usually requires fluency in the language of the country where you are based. So for many science-related jobs and other careers that take you overseas, language skills are a great asset.

There are a number of undergraduate courses that will give you the chance to study languages as well as science. These could be combined courses in science and languages, but more often they are full science degree courses with language study alongside. Languages at A/AS level are not always required in order to do this kind of course, although clearly they would be a help. Many students complete their courses successfully with only a GCSE base in languages, but this does involve extra work.

International opportunities for students

Studying abroad will help you develop an international perspective, which may be useful, if not essential, for many scientific careers. You could consider enrolling on an undergraduate or postgraduate course offered by an overseas institution, although this may prove an undertaking too far for most people – particularly due to financial, logistical and language issues. A simpler option is to consider a course at a UK institution that incorporates overseas study as part of its syllabus. There are several science degree programmes that include a period of study abroad and these vary in what they have to offer. Your home university may have links with several overseas institutions for you to choose between, in Europe and beyond; you may spend a single term abroad, or a whole academic year; and your preliminary studies may need to incorporate language lessons, depending on your chosen destination.

If your university offers you a placement in Europe, this may be through the **Erasmus** programme. As a UK student, provided you spend a full academic year on an Erasmus programme, you do not have to pay any tuition fees for that year to either your UK or overseas institution. All eligible UK students receive an Erasmus grant, which contributes towards the extra costs arising from studying abroad, in addition to any student grant or loan to which you are normally entitled from UK sources. The Erasmus programme is open to undergraduates and postgraduates up to doctorate level and is administered by the British Council. For more information, see: www.britishcouncil.org/erasmus.

Another option for students is to undertake a work placement abroad during college vacations. The International Association for the Exchange of Students for Technical Experience (IAESTE), for example, can help science students find vacation work abroad during their degree studies. Find out more on: www.iaeste.org.uk.

International research opportunities

As a research scientist, it is possible to collaborate on international projects – based either in the UK or abroad. The following are just a few examples of organisations that offer funding for international research and collaboration.

- The **European Space Agency** offers research fellowships for applicants with a doctorate in space science to undertake research projects at an institution outside their home country.

- The **British Council** aims to build cultural links between Britain and the rest of the world and operates in over 100 countries. In the scientific arena, it helps UK researchers work on international collaborations by, for example, funding exchange visits and networking conferences.

- The **Royal Society** operates many different funding schemes, including early career fellowship schemes and mobility grant schemes, which offer financial support for overseas travel and international collaboration on long- and short-term scientific projects.

- The **Wellcome Trust** is a charity that funds biomedical research, both in the UK and abroad, and can offer financial backing to researchers in the form of international fellowships.

- **NATO** (North Atlantic Treaty Organisation), through its Science for Peace and Security (SPS) Committee, provides grants to scientists involved in international research into defence against terrorism and other security threats.

The European Commission actively supports the free movement of scientists within Europe through the EURAXESS programme. This comprises a variety of initiatives, including:

- an online job site for European research posts and funding opportunities

- a network of service centres to help researchers plan all the practical aspects of their move to a foreign country

- a set of principles and requirements relating to the recruitment and employment of researchers, with the aim of making research an attractive career option.

Visit the EURAXESS - *Researchers in Motion* website for full details: http://ec.europa.eu/euraxess.

Working overseas

As a science graduate, there are many opportunities open to you if you wish to work abroad, either on a permanent basis, or as part of a UK-based job that involves occasional international travel, or through casual or voluntary work.

Scientists may find international opportunities with commercial organisations that operate in the agricultural, pharmaceutical, petrochemical, mining and extraction industries, for example. Many agencies, consultancies and charities involved in ecology, environmental protection and healthcare also recruit UK science graduates to work overseas.

The public sector offers some overseas opportunities for those with a scientific background. For example, the European Commission employs its own scientists and technologists in a wide range disciplines, both in Brussels and at research centres across the EU. While the Department for International Development (DFID - the government department that seeks to tackle world poverty) has offices in a number of developing countries, including several in Asia and Africa. The DFID recruits staff for work in developing countries from a wide range of backgrounds, including agriculture, forestry, fisheries, engineering, and health.

Career profiles

The following profiles describe the experiences of six, real-life scientists. While they each have a science degree, their interests have led them into quite different career areas, and in some cases onto postgraduate study and work overseas. Their profiles may help provide an insight into the reality of a career in science.

Dr Nizar Ben Ayed

Job title: MAST magnetics physicist

Employer: United Kingdom Atomic Energy Authority

Post-16 qualifications: International Baccalaureate (mathematics, physics, chemistry, computing, languages). A levels in maths and physics.

Degree: MSci physics with industrial experience

Postgraduate qualifications: PhD in plasma physics

As part of my undergraduate degree course, I did a 12-month placement at the United Kingdom Atomic Energy Authority – one of the world's leading fusion research laboratories. During this time, fusion research took my interest: I was inspired by the scientists and engineers who were working with collaborators around the globe to develop fusion as a new source of clean energy for future power stations. As a result, I decided to do a PhD in the field of plasma physics. After which, I was offered a position on a full-time basis.

I always knew I didn't want a boring city job, and that I wanted to work in science to contribute to society and mankind on some of the most worrying issues. Since the need for energy is so great and growing so rapidly around the world, I decided to dedicate my career to this worthy scientific challenge.

Broadly speaking, as an experimental plasma physicist, my research concentrates on applying experimental plasma physics to investigate how to control and stabilise fusion plasmas. More specifically, I am responsible for the development and maintenance of magnetic diagnostics. These systems are essential for the safety and protection of the experimental facility, real-time control, measurement and stabilisation of the complex instabilities that occur in fusion plasmas.

It's essential for this type of work that you have the desire to keep learning. A significant proportion of what I do draws on a range of scientific disciplines including physics, maths, engineering and computer programming. Some of these are taught at university, but I learned (and continue to learn) a great deal while 'doing the job', and I find this particularly appealing.

Communication and presentation skills are also vital. I have developed good people skills that are invaluable when it comes to presenting and defending my work to my peer group and external bodies of scientists.

Research relies a great deal on teamwork. Most work is based on other people's results, which means working closely with my colleagues to build on the foundations of what is already known and find answers to unsolved problems. I also find myself working in a lab, which can be quite lonely. However, overall success is achieved only through endurance and motivation, which can only be provided by a strong team unit whether working together or working alone.

There are many aspects of my job that I like. Mainly, it is the freedom to ask questions and find out answers. I also enjoy the interaction with my colleagues. Travel to conferences to communicate my findings to the international fusion community is also extremely rewarding, since you get to discover different parts of the world and forge friendships on professional and personal levels.

Finding out the answers to the complex physics phenomena that occur in fusion plasmas is a difficult task. It involves working on cutting-edge physics problems and brings its own challenges. I feel strongly about my work and therefore lots of hours, energy and determination are required. The ability to bounce back from minor setbacks is also important, as sometimes it is easy to lose sight of the big picture when your research appears to hit a stumbling block.

While science does open a broad range of non-science career paths, I hope to stay working on the problem of developing nuclear fusion as a new source of clean energy.

Christopher Curd

Job title: Trainee clinical vascular scientist

Employer: NHS

Post-16 qualifications: A levels in maths, further maths, chemistry, biology and general studies. AS level in psychology.

Degree: BSc Zoology – Durham University

Postgraduate qualifications: MSc vascular ultrasound, King's College London (I've just finished my second year of a three-year, part-time course)

In my third year as an undergraduate, I saw the job of trainee vascular scientist advertised through the NHS Clinical Scientist Recruitment Scheme. I wanted some kind of career related to science, and at the time I didn't want to do research. I'd done a project on Reynolds syndrome (a vascular condition causing spasm of small blood vessels) one summer, which I'd found really interesting, so when I saw this job was science based and in an area I had some experience in, I jumped at it. Also the pay wasn't bad either! I'm currently half-way through my three-year training contract.

In this role, I'm responsible for performing and interpreting ultrasound scans of the vascular system (arteries and veins). This includes, but is in no way limited to, scanning the arteries in the necks of stroke victims, scanning veins for blood clots, looking at leg arteries of people with poor circulation, and finding the source of varicose veins. As you advance in your career you are also encouraged to undertake research and clinical audits.

Technically, you don't need any specialist qualifications to do vascular ultrasound. However, most people will have, at least, a postgraduate certificate and have completed the Society for Vascular Technology's programme to become an Accredited Vascular Scientist (AVS). As for other skills and knowledge, you need to be able to understand the wide breadth of science involved in the job (including physics, pathology, anatomy etc), have good hand-to-eye coordination, excellent people skills (especially with older people), the ability to communicate (both with patients and doctors), compassion and patience, and to be able to cope with what can be at times a demanding job.

One of the things I like about this work is being able to play a role in the diagnosis and treatment of patients. It's particularly important to me that I am responsible for the interpretation and reporting of my scans (unlike radiographers), and, as such, I get to own my work. In my job you also get to develop relationships with those patients that you see regularly. In a similar vein, you work very closely with the vascular surgeons.

The main challenge in this role is learning to be patient, both with those people that you are scanning (who often can't or won't help themselves) and with people, such as doctors, who can be demanding of your time. For me as a trainee, it's also hard balancing a full-time job with studying for an MSc and professional accreditation. I'm lucky as I will often get one day off a week to study, but this isn't the case for everyone.

Once I'm accredited and have finished my MSc, hopefully I will spend a few years just working at the hospital where I am now, enjoying not having any academic commitments. After that, I could look for a senior vascular scientist post elsewhere. On the other hand, I could look at going into research, either in vascular ultrasound, or something related, such as cardiovascular biology.

Science has always interested me. I remember when I was growing up I had a particular interest in natural history and astronomy, and I even I told my parents that I wanted to be a scientist when I was older. The thing that really excites me is how science provides us with a set of tools to understand the amazing world around us, which in turn, proves to be even more amazing than we'd first imagined. In my current job there are so many different fields of science that come together to get the job done and I find that really exciting.

Dr Lionel Hill

Job title: Metabolite service manager

Employer: John Innes Centre, Norwich – an independent, international centre of excellence in plant science and microbiology. The John Innes

Centre is an Institute of the Biotechnology & Biological Sciences Research Council.

Post-16 qualifications: A levels in biology, chemistry and physics

Degree: Degree in natural sciences - University of Cambridge

This is a very general science degree, which allows you to mix-and-match different subjects. I specialised in plant science in my third year because I liked its agricultural connection.

After my degree, I moved to Norwich to do a PhD at the John Innes Centre, working on the biochemistry of starch synthesis in pea seeds. From here, I went on to a postdoctoral research post in Heidelberg, Germany. We were interested in how potatoes become sweet when stored in the cold, which is a big problem for chips and crisps (it gives them a black colour when fried). Germany was an eye-opening experience scientifically, but for me it was also a wonderful opportunity to cycle to work through vineyards, to learn a language and to live in a different culture.

When my research post ended, I took a job as a research assistant back at the John Innes Centre. At the same time, the field of 'metabolomics' was blossoming; this is the untargeted measurement of lots of chemicals in a plant (or urine, or whatever) with a view to hunting down changes in metabolism, or identifying disease. It meant we urgently needed chemical analysis and, building on my time in Germany, I volunteered for my current job, running our analytical service.

With two colleagues, I measure whatever chemicals our clients present us with: antibiotics; synthetic chemicals brewed up by the chemists; the substances that give plants their flavours or discourage pests; and so on. My personal expertise is liquid chromatography coupled to mass spectrometry. I also run the lab, which means a certain amount of paperwork, meetings and financial work, as well as advising managers on where our lab is going, and what we need.

My job needs a mix of both personal and technical skills. On the personal side, it's about communication, and a careful and organised attitude to work. I'm often working with many clients simultaneously, and need to be aware of what they want, and the problems they are having. Accurate results require care at every stage; it can feel quite pressurised at times. On the technical side, the job requires a good understanding of the instruments, and understanding of both biology and chemistry.

I love the variety of my work and the feeling that at least some of what I do might, one day, be of bigger benefit. I enjoy having to think, and the moments when we get a beautifully clear result that makes you realise why a particular chemical behaves in a particular way. I feel lucky that I work with others; the benefit is the same as playing a duet: with no extra ability, you get twice as much music.

However, the equipment necessary in an analytical lab is becoming more expensive and sophisticated, which makes it harder to maintain a competitive lab and I find the process of competing for resources challenging. Funding can change very rapidly. My field has expanded enormously in just ten years, and will certainly change as much in the next ten. Labs will have to share big equipment, and there will have to be a balance between academic freedom and a need for business considerations. There will be more use of computational biology, using computer simulations, but there will be new areas of experiment too (such as mass spectrometry for imaging tissues). I expect we will see more opportunities for people with skills in more than one discipline –biologists with excellent chemical backgrounds, or good maths, for example.

Various people have influenced my career choices over the years – my chemistry teacher at school, my director of studies at Cambridge, my PhD supervisor and the group in Germany. I also have a great interest in technology and love to understand how things work. I think science careers often have a natural flow from school through to your first research post, and it's easy to drift. Sometimes I wish I had taken more responsibility for my career and made more assertive choices; but then I look at the fun I've had, the friends I've met and the job I'm in, and I realise that I probably couldn't have planned anything better.

Vicki Hodges

Job title: Attitude and orbit control systems (AOCS) engineer

Employer: EADS Astrium – a company that designs, manufactures, launches and operates spacecraft for telecommunications, military and scientific applications

Post-16 qualifications: A levels in physics, maths and history. A/S levels in chemistry and archaeology.

Degree: BSc physics with satellite technology (included a year in industry) – University of Surrey

I always enjoyed physics and chemistry at school and was fascinated with space. My physics teacher encouraged me to pursue a career in physics and helped me realise that it offered lots of varied opportunities. The great thing about physics is that it's an incredibly broad subject with many different specialisms. I also love the fact that physics can explain anything and everything you want to know about the world and the universe!

My career in the space industry began with a year spent working in Germany, as part of my degree course. I worked for a company that was involved with a project on behalf of the Canadian Space Agency. I was part of the spacecraft simulation team developing and testing the spacecraft simulator to ensure it behaved in a realistic way.

I think that undertaking this work experience was really worthwhile as, even with a BSc rather than an MEng degree, I was offered a job with EADS Astrium and started six weeks after graduating. I joined the company on their Graduate Development Programme, a two-year scheme that enables you to experience various parts of the organisation, before deciding where your interests lie. I started by spending six months with the AOCS group, then spent two shorter placements on the commercial and contracts side of the business, and with an engineering team in Toulouse, France. I'm now back with the AOCS team in Stevenage, where I am involved in the GAIA spacecraft project, which is a European Space Agency mission to map the location and movement of one billion stars in the Milky Way.

The AOCS is a system that controls the location and orientation of spacecraft in space. Spacecraft need to work autonomously and react logically to different scenarios; there is no-one up there driving them! For example, their solar panels have to face the sun at all times and their telescopes have to be pointed in precisely the right direction and remain steady enough to collect useable data. The AOCS for GAIA must be accurate to within 100 milliarcseconds (that equates to 1/36000th of a degree)! I'm part of the team that designs and tests these systems.

Most of the work is done using computers to simulate and analyse the performance of the AOCS design. We also conduct feasibility studies on systems for future projects that may be launched 15-20 years from now! Every day is different – we know what the 'headline' tasks are, but how we go about achieving them constantly evolves. There's a lot of autonomy in this role, how you set about completing your own tasks is down to you. However, we also work very closely as a team – coming together to solve problems and share our findings, so good communication is very important.

For this particular type of work, you need an interest in space as well as a degree in engineering, maths or physics. You also have to enjoy number crunching and getting stuck into lots of detail! It helps to have a good understanding of all the mathematical concepts that you are taught during your degree.

Sometimes it can be easy to forget what your starting point was, as you have become so embroiled in the detail. It can also be a challenge meeting the schedule, as you can't always plan for every eventuality. Having a flexible approach is crucial, as, occasionally, you have to just let things go and move onto other tasks.

As far as my future is concerned, I'd like to get as much AOCS experience as possible. As I joined this project at quite a late stage in its lifecycle, I'd like to join the next project right from the start of the design process. I'm also interested in public engagement and have been involved in outreach programmes that promote physics and maths in schools, which is something I want to continue doing!

Dr Louissa Marsh

Job title: Court reporting forensic scientist

Employer: LGC Forensics - a privately-owned forensic science service provider

Post-16 qualifications: HNC chemistry

Degree: BSc chemistry

Postgraduate qualifications: PhD in material chemistry

I left school halfway through my A levels in biology, chemistry and physics, due to personal reasons. I then found work as an apprentice paint scientist for an international chemical company. This enabled me to learn a trade in the laboratory, while also taking an HNC on day release. The course was valuable not only for my work in paint formulation, but also because it made it possible for me to move onto a degree course and continue my education while also caring for my daughter. I achieved a BSc in chemistry, also taken part time on day release. I then undertook a full-time research doctorate, which lasted three years.

In my role as a forensic scientist, a criminal case is assigned to me and I have to investigate the items submitted to try to find and understand any evidence that is present. My findings are written into a court statement, which can be offered in evidence and may either be read out or I may have to give this evidence in person. An expert forensic scientist is allowed to provide an opinion on these findings, which means experts can and, often, do disagree! Cases vary from 'simple' criminal damage cases, for example when a house window is broken, to multiple murders where the evidence can be extremely complicated and may take years to investigate fully.

Forensic science can be perceived as glamorous with excitement and fast-track results round every corner. But the real work can often be frustratingly slow and laborious, requiring meticulous note-taking and repeated checking of each and every finding. It's therefore important that you can pay attention to detail and stay calm under pressure. You also need knowledge of the analytical techniques used; a good grounding in chemistry, biology and physics provide the best start to someone embarking on a forensic science career. Communicating complex scientific reasoning in simple terms can be problematic, but is an important part of the job. Skills in English language would therefore help, plus the confidence to stick to your guns when being questioned or criticised.

Forensic science is a huge, broad subject and it is not possible to be an 'expert' in every field. Most people specialise and budding forensic scientists develop into experts by gaining qualifications and experience at every level. The skills needed to be a forensic scientist: meticulous note-taking, observation, concentration for long periods of time, written and oral presentation skills, confidence and the understanding that no-one can ever know everything, are transferable to any scientific field.

Forensic investigations have to be performed quickly, in order to catch suspects without delay and keep them in custody while evidence is gathered, among other reasons. Keeping a level head and being able to prioritise, manage your time and delegate are extremely important. No investigation is run by just one person; a team is almost always involved and you must be able to work successfully with other investigators, whether these are colleagues or police officers. Most forensic work is done out of the public eye and acknowledgement by the public or media is extremely rare.

The work is extremely varied; every case presents new challenges and problems, and this constant variation means I never stop learning. I also feel that forensic scientists have a genuine place in the judicial system and contribute to a safer society. In this job, every day is different and every single case involves real people, an important thing to remember. I believe that forensic science teaches you to examine a problem from many different angles. Often there is not a concise answer to specific problems, only opinions and hypothesis.

Science is all about experimentation. Trying things out, seeing things happen, working out what went wrong. Watching fireworks, listening to explosions, breaking open rocks to see fossils, the subject is huge! Small children naturally find out about the world through play and by asking questions, but this curiosity can start to fizzle out as children get older and become restricted in what they are allowed to do. I was extremely lucky with my mentors and teachers, and the need to understand and to experiment has never left me. Juggling responsibilities, such as those relating to becoming a parent, can often become a stumbling block in continuing education, but does not have to prevent it. The career choices I made were influenced by the availability of continuing education, while being able to earn at the same time. Science is all about continually learning and constantly questioning and discovering, at any age.

Dr Sarah Polack

Job title: Lecturer

Employer: London School of Hygiene & Tropical Medicine (LSHTM)

Post-16 qualifications: English, biology and geography A levels

Degree: BSc biological sciences

Postgraduate qualifications: MSc in the control of infectious diseases; PhD in public health/epidemiology.

My degree in biological sciences at the University of Liverpool suited me, as it was broad based and geared to students who wanted to study biology but were not yet certain in which particular area they wanted to specialise. During the course, I specialised in zoology. As part of my degree, I took a course in parasitology run by the Liverpool School of Tropical Medicine and my final-year dissertation involved investigating women's ideas about health in pregnancy. Through these I developed a great interest in public health – an area that combined my interests in biology, disease and people.

Following my degree, in order to explore this interest in public health and epidemiology, I worked for a year at the University of Bristol's Department of Social Medicine. I was employed as a clerical assistant on health research projects and learned a great deal about what was involved in health research. Through speaking to people both at Liverpool and Bristol University, I learned more about the LSHTM and found a number of courses that seemed really interesting and would enable me to further my interests and qualify me to work within the field of public health in developing countries. I took a one-year MSc in the control of infectious diseases, a course that aimed to bridge the disciplines of epidemiology, public health and laboratory sciences. Following completion of my MSc, I worked as a research assistant at the LSHTM on a number of projects, including a study of risk factors for highland malaria in Kenya; exploring the relationship between trachoma (an eye disease) and household access to water in Tanzania; and mapping the global distribution of trachoma using geographical information systems.

More recently, I worked on a study exploring the impact of cataract surgery on poverty and quality of life in Kenya, Bangladesh and the Philippines. This project formed my PhD, which I undertook as a part-time student at LSHTM and completed in 2008. I am currently a lecturer at the LSHTM. My job involves research – mainly on diabetes and diabetic retinopathy – and includes fieldwork for data collection (most recently in Mexico), data analysis and writing articles for publication. I also teach MSc students.

There are challenges in my job. For example, there is always a lot to do (!); funding is not usually guaranteed for more than two or three years and frequent travel can be quite disruptive. However, my job is varied, which keeps it interesting, and the LSHTM is an exciting place to be in terms of its contribution to international public health. I feel privileged to be able to spend time working in different countries as part of my research, and really enjoy teaching students from all around the world.

Section 2
Science-related careers

Chapter six

Science careers: general

This chapter describes many of the science careers open to you. As long as your studies are broadly in the biological, chemical or physical sciences, you should be able to find jobs in this list that will suit you. In some cases, entry may be possible directly after completing your degree; in others a relevant postgraduate qualification may be required. Check exact entry requirements with employers, as they do vary.

The career ideas included in this chapter are:

- acoustician
- agricultural scientist
- analytical chemist
- arboriculturist
- astronomer/space scientist

- biochemist
- biotechnologist
- botanist/plant scientist
- clinical perfusion scientist
- clinical scientist
- colour technologist
- conservator
- consumer scientist
- cosmetic scientist
- environmental health practitioner
- environmental scientist
- ergonomist
- food scientist/technologist
- forensic scientist
- forester
- geoscientist
- health and safety inspector
- horticulturist
- hydrologist
- industrial chemist
- laboratory technician
- landscape scientist
- materials scientist
- medical physicist
- meteorologist
- nuclear scientist
- occupational hygienist
- patent attorney

- patent examiner
- pharmacologist
- public analyst
- research scientist
- sport and exercise scientist
- surveyor
- technical brewer
- toxicologist
- waste/recycling manager
- zoologist.

Acoustician

Acousticians are specialists in sound who are concerned with acoustics, noise and vibration. Sound can have a major impact on the quality of our lives – in both positive and negative ways. For example, a well-designed concert hall can give immense pleasure to an audience of music lovers. However, in other circumstances, excessive noise can cause stress and discomfort and, in extreme situations, can lead to hearing loss. Minimising unwanted noise and vibration is therefore important in many situations, for factory workers on a production line, passengers on an aeroplane and so on.

Employment opportunities for acousticians are mostly found in industry and commerce, consultancy work, education and research and the public sector. The exact nature of an acoustician's work varies according to the setting in which they are employed – there are roles relating to aerodynamics, architectural acoustics, broadcasting, engineering, environmental noise control, health and safety, music technology, product design, sonar, speech recognition and ultrasonics.

Acoustic work often involves being a member of a team of professionals from a range of disciplines. You may be required to undertake research, help design new products or buildings, understand and advise on relevant legislation, or act as an expert witness in court cases. Recent EU directives on machinery, factory and vehicle noise mean that opportunities in this area of work are increasing.

Entry qualifications

It may be possible to find work in acoustics with a science degree; however, it is more likely that you will need a specialist qualification in the area of acoustics, noise control, or sound and vibration. There are many relevant postgraduate courses available, for which a science degree (particularly in a physics-related subject) would be acceptable for entry.

Acousticians need good teamworking and analytical skills and the ability to solve problems creatively. Accuracy and attention to detail, as well as IT skills, are also important.

Training and career development

The Institute of Acoustics (IOA) offers several courses and qualifications for trainee acousticians. For example, the IOA Diploma in acoustics and noise control is a one-year, part-time course that offers partial exemption from certain MSc courses. Various degree subjects are accepted for entry onto the Diploma course, including science subjects.

The Institute of Sound and Vibration Research (ISVR) at the University of Southampton offers several programmes of study, including the MSc in sound and vibration studies. This is open to physics graduates (as well as engineering and maths graduates).

Progression may be to a supervisory or senior management position, or by specialising in a particular branch of acoustics. With relevant experience, it may be possible to work on a self-employed basis as a consultant in private practice.

Finding vacancies

Vacancies are advertised on the IOA website and in their bi-monthly publication *Acoustics Bulletin* (available to order online). Employers may also advertise vacancies on their own websites or through specialist recruitment agencies and online job sites.

While at university, or as a recent graduate, you can access information about potential employers and current graduate vacancies through your university careers service. Further information about the help available through university careers services is provided in Chapter three.

Sources of further information

Institute of Acoustics (IOA) – tel: 01727 848195. www.ioa.org.uk

Institute of Sound and Vibration Research (ISVR) – tel: 023 8059 2294. www.isvr.soton.ac.uk

Agricultural scientist

Farming is a major industry within the UK, contributing almost £6 billion to the economy every year. However, it faces many economic pressures, for example, from cheap foreign imports, animal and plant diseases, changing consumer tastes, adverse weather conditions and so on. Improving the yield from crops and livestock, safely and cost-effectively, is an ongoing quest and is at the heart of much of the scientific endeavour in this sector. Protecting and improving the environment, guaranteeing the health and welfare of animals and developing biofuels are among other important areas of scientific research. As an agricultural scientist, your work could involve laboratory-based research or field trials involving some outdoor work.

Opportunities for agricultural scientists exist with a range of employers. Commercial concerns, such as industrial firms, agrochemical companies, plant breeders, seed specialists, livestock producers and research associations, for example, need people to research and develop new products and new techniques. The Biotechnology and Biological Sciences Research Council funds research projects involving scientists from a range of disciplines, with the aim of improving food quality and safety. Advisory and consultancy services provide support to farming businesses in relation to technical developments and policy changes; ADAS is one of the largest and best-known agencies. The Civil Service, among other employers, offers opportunities for scientists to work in testing and inspecting agricultural produce. For example, Defra (the Department for Environment, Food and Rural Affairs) – and its many executive agencies – is concerned with policy making and regulation enforcement.

Entry qualifications

It's possible to begin a career in agriculture with a degree in an agricultural subject, an applied science, or in subjects such as biology, chemistry, biochemistry, microbiology, plant science, animal science, biotechnology, genetics or soil science. Postgraduate qualifications are often required.

As well as excellent research skills and scientific understanding, this type of work obviously requires an interest in the environment, plants and animals. The pace of change in the sector means that you will need to be flexible; you will also need to understand the regulatory environment that you will be operating within.

Training and career development

Specialist training will vary according to the exact nature of your employment and is likely to involve short courses, conferences, etc. By undertaking continuing professional development (CPD), it may be possible to work towards chartered status of a relevant society or institute, such as the Society of Biology.

For those with relevant qualifications and experience, there are opportunities to work overseas, including within developing countries. Other options for career development include agricultural journalism and teaching/lecturing.

Finding vacancies

Jobs are advertised in publications such as *Farmers Weekly* and associated websites. Employers are also likely to advertise positions on their own websites or through specialist recruitment agencies. Details of how to apply for jobs in the Civil Service and other public agencies can be found at www.civilservice.gov.uk/jobs.

While at university, or as a recent graduate, you can access information about potential employers and current graduate vacancies through your university careers service. Further information about the help available through university careers services is provided in Chapter three.

Sources of further information

ADAS – tel: 0845 766 0085. www.adas.co.uk

The Biotechnology and Biological Sciences Research Council (BBSRC) – tel: 01793 413200. www.bbsrc.ac.uk

Defra (Department for Environment, Food and Rural Affairs) – tel: 08459 335577. www.defra.gov.uk

Lantra – the Sector Skills Council for the environmental and land-based sector. Tel: 0845 707 8007. www.lantra.co.uk and www.afuturein.com

National Farmers' Union (NFU) – tel: 024 7685 8500. www.nfuonline.com

Society of Biology – tel: 020 7936 5900. www.societyofbiology.org

Analytical chemist

As an analytical chemist, your role would be to test and identify the chemical composition of specific substances as well as assessing how substances behave under different conditions. There are many chemical tests that can be used; your expertise would be required to select the most appropriate tests and to carry them out methodically and with great precision. The work involves report writing and, possibly, the development of new analytical techniques.

Analytical chemists may be employed in a wide range of settings. In the **pharmaceutical industry** their role may be to monitor the quality of drugs and assess their stability. In the **healthcare sector**, analytical chemists work in hospital laboratories analysing samples from patients in order to assist in diagnoses. In **public health laboratories**, chemists test samples of any substance that has been suspected of endangering health including contaminated drinking water, chemical spillages, substandard animal feed etc. Analytical chemists are often employed within the **manufacturing sector** (including food, drink, cosmetics, agrochemical, petrochemical and polymer manufacture) in order to help develop processes, monitor the quality of raw materials and finished products, and verify contents/ingredients for licensing, if necessary. In **forensic laboratories**, analytical chemists analyse samples collected as evidence from crime scenes, such as blood, fibres, traces from firearms, poisons etc.

Entry qualifications

Entry is possible with a degree in a chemical science; particularly relevant subjects include chemistry, analytical chemistry, applied chemistry, biochemistry, pharmaceutical science, forensic science, food science and materials science. Employers may expect applicants to have at least a 2:1 degree.

Analytical chemists need a high level of practical skill and an ability to accurately record and interpret results. Previous work experience gained in a laboratory may be useful. Problem-solving skills are essential for this type of work, and you will need to be comfortable working in a team as well as independently.

Training and career development

Training usually involves on-the-job learning as well as short courses and technical instruction in how to use specialist equipment and computer software. You may also need to attend conferences to keep up to date with developments in your field and short courses to learn about other topics, such as specific research techniques. As a member of the Royal Society of Chemistry (RSC), it is possible to work towards chartered chemist status (CChem). This requires an RSC-accredited degree or equivalent in the first instance.

It may be possible to undertake a postgraduate qualification such as a masters degree or even a PhD, on a part-time basis, while in employment. These may be required for more senior posts.

Finding vacancies

Vacancies are advertised in the RSC journal *Chemistry World*, and on its associated website, www.rsc.org./chemistryworld. Employers may also advertise vacancies on their own websites or through specialist recruitment agencies and online job sites.

While at university, or as a recent graduate, you can access information about potential employers and current graduate vacancies through your university careers service. Further information about the help available through university careers services is provided in Chapter three.

Sources of further information

Association of the British Pharmaceutical Industry (ABPI) - tel: 0870 890 4333. www.abpi.org.uk and http://abpi-careers.org.uk

Cogent - the Sector Skills Council for the chemicals, pharmaceuticals, polymers etc industries. Tel: 01925 515200. www.cogent-careers.com

Forensic Science Service - www.forensic.gov.uk

Royal Society of Chemistry (RSC) - tel: 020 7437 8656. www.rsc.org

Arboriculturist

Many trees and shrubs are planted to enhance our surroundings - along roadsides, in parks and gardens, and as woodlands. Arboriculture is the cultivation and management of trees in these amenity settings, rather than for timber production. It is closely linked with forestry, horticulture and landscape design and construction.

Arboriculturists may design and plan planting projects, selecting plants and detailing maintenance plans. They also undertake surveys and inspections to identify pests and diseases, safety issues, subsidence risks and so on. The work can involve advising on tree preservation or supervising tree felling. Some arboriculturists specialise in community woodlands, or in the reclamation of industrial sites. The role combines office-based activities – report writing, costing work, liaising with other professionals etc, as well as practical, outdoor work – visiting sites and climbing trees in order to conduct inspections.

Arboriculturists can work for local government planning departments, as well as for major landowners, such as the National Trust. Landscaping contractors and building developers may also employ arboricultural specialists. Many arboriculturists undertake consultancy work, either self-employed or as a member of a consultancy firm.

Entry qualifications

A degree in forestry or arboriculture would be preferable for entry to this type of work; alternatively, degree subjects such as biology, ecology, plant science, land management, horticulture or agriculture may be acceptable. The Institute of Chartered Foresters (ICF) accredits certain degree courses.

Knowledge of the biology of trees is obviously critical for this type of work, as is an understanding of health and safety legislation, planning regulations and tree preservation regulations. Previous practical experience is definitely an asset, as is a driving licence. You will need to be physically fit, and happy to work outdoors and at height.

Training and career development

Training is likely to be on the job and through specialist short courses. You may be required to undertake practical training in the use of chainsaws, pesticides, mobile platforms, ropes for climbing etc.

With an ICF-accredited degree plus further training and experience, it is possible to gain chartered arboriculturist status.

With experience and suitable qualifications, it may be possible to progress to management or to start your own consultancy firm and become self-employed.

Finding vacancies

Local authority vacancies are advertised on www.LGjobs.com. Jobs are also advertised in the trade journal *Horticulture Week* and its associated website. Employers may also advertise vacancies on their own websites or through specialist recruitment agencies and online job sites.

While at university, or as a recent graduate, you can access information about potential employers and current graduate vacancies through your university careers service. Further information about the help available through university careers services is provided in Chapter three.

Sources of further information

Arboricultural Association – tel 01242 522152. www.trees.org.uk

Institute of Chartered Foresters – tel: 0131 240 1425. www.charteredforesters.org

Lantra – the Sector Skills Council for the environmental and land-based sector. Tel: 0845 707 8007. www.lantra.co.uk

Astronomer/Space scientist

There are many different scientific disciplines concerned with the study of the universe; together these are known as space science. Astronomy – the study of stars, planets, comets etc – is just one of these disciplines. Astronomers and space scientists undertake both observational and theoretical work. They analyse data that is collected by electronic detectors on ground-based telescopes, observatories on orbiting satellites, and recording instruments carried by spacecraft and on probes that are sent far into space.

Measurements obtained from only a few hours' observations can take several months to analyse, using the most advanced mathematical and statistical computer analysis. The results can reveal exciting new findings, but there's still a lot to be discovered about our universe and its origins.

Almost all astronomers and space scientists employed in this country work in university research departments and government-funded establishments. Examples are the UK Astronomy Technology Centre in Edinburgh, and the Rutherford Appleton Laboratory near Didcot in Oxfordshire, which are the responsibility of the Science & Technology Facilities Council. Around 25 universities in the UK have astronomy and space science research groups.

There are a few related posts in the commercial sector, working in aerospace or on communications satellites etc, and space tourism is fast becoming a reality.

Further afield, the European Space Agency, with its headquarters in Paris, offers a range of opportunities, including a trainee programme for masters-level graduates looking for their first job in space science, fixed-term research fellowships and some permanent positions.

Entry qualifications

You need at least a 2:1 degree, and usually also a higher degree for entry into this area of work. First degrees may be in astrophysics or physics, although some branches of chemistry can also be useful (as indeed can maths, computer science or engineering). Some degrees combine astronomy, astrophysics or space science with physics, maths and other subjects. There are also degree courses relating to space technology. A degree in the earth sciences may be useful if, later, you want to study planets and meteorites. Look carefully at the content of each course to see how broad-based or specialist it is. It's possible to specialise at the postgraduate stage.

Astronomers and space scientists need to have enquiring minds, excellent powers of observation, patience, analytical skills, computer literacy and good communication skills.

Training and career development

Postgraduate training is usually undertaken in a university research department and leads to a PhD. This involves at least three years' work, conducting research and writing a thesis, under the supervision of a member of the academic team.

Once you have gained a PhD, the usual route is to find work through a research fellowship. These are funded by universities, research councils or other organisations and operate on a fixed-term basis. Beyond this, you could consider a permanent academic career with a university, starting with a position as a lecturer, before promotion to senior lecturer and then professor.

Finding vacancies

Opportunities in astronomy and space science are very limited. Quite a large proportion of people completing a first degree in this field continue to study for a higher degree, with only a few finding relevant employment each year within the various research organisations.

You can subscribe to a job alert service through the Royal Astronomical Society website. Employers may also advertise vacancies on their own websites.

While at university, or as a recent graduate, you can access information about potential employers and current graduate vacancies through your university careers service. Further information about the help available through university careers services is provided in Chapter three.

Sources of further information

British Astronomical Association – an association for keen amateurs. Tel: 020 7734 4145. www.britastro.org

European Space Agency – tel: +33 1 5369 7654. www.esa.int

Institute of Physics – tel: 020 7470 4800. www.iop.org

Royal Astronomical Society – tel: 020 7734 4582. www.ras.org.uk

Science & Technology Facilities Council – tel: 01793 442000. www.stfc.ac.uk

Biochemist

Biochemists are interested in every aspect of living things, such as animals, plants and micro-organisms, and how they are made up. Biochemists try to understand how living things work at the molecular level and investigate biological processes. The work has practical applications in areas such as the environment, agriculture, horticulture, medicine, veterinary science, plant research, and food, pharmaceutical, fertiliser and pesticide production.

A few examples of the different ways biochemical research can be used include making genetic changes to crops and livestock, monitoring the metabolism of athletes or the development of children, or fighting disease in plants, animals and people.

Biochemistry is a practical science that is laboratory-based. The work may involve preparing samples of animal or plant tissue or fluids for experimental testing, analysis and screening, using the very latest technology. You may need to handle animals for research purposes, work with hazardous substances or infectious micro-organisms.

In industry – the main areas of employment are the research and development of new products, production processes, and quality control. Some biochemists spend their entire career doing this sort of work, while others move on to general managerial roles.

In research - there are opportunities in various research institutes, and in government departments. Universities also offer research positions, which may be sponsored by bodies such as the Research Councils, or by charities such as the Wellcome Trust.

In laboratories - clinical biochemists work in medical laboratories, either in universities or in the NHS, undertaking biochemical analyses to help in the diagnosis and management of disease. There are also some opportunities in veterinary science laboratories. Some forensic science laboratories offer opportunities for biochemistry graduates.

In education - there are limited opportunities for lecturing in higher education, for which a higher degree is essential. Although biochemistry is not taught as a subject in schools and colleges, biochemistry graduates can train to teach subjects such as biology, chemistry and science.

Entry qualifications

Degrees are available in biochemistry as a single subject or combined with another science. Biological science degree courses with a high biochemistry content are also suitable for entry into this area of work.

It is important for this type of work that you have good powers of observation and concentration. You need to be able to work accurately and use very complex equipment. Biochemists also need the ability to work under their own initiative, as well as in a team, and to be able to communicate well with non-specialists.

Training and career development

On-the-job training may involve learning about specialist equipment and computer software, as well as health and safety aspects. You may also need to attend conferences to keep up to date with developments in this field and short courses to learn about other topics, such as specific research techniques. Once in employment, it may be possible to study for a postgraduate qualification on a part-time basis. A higher degree, such as a PhD or MSc in biochemistry, may be beneficial for career progression or essential for some roles, such as for university lecturer.

Trainee clinical biochemists in the NHS follow a structured training programme, rotating between different laboratories within their region, while studying for a postgraduate qualification.

Finding vacancies

Vacancies are advertised in publications such as *New Scientist* and its associated website, by specialist recruitment agencies, on specialist online job sites, in the appointments sections of certain daily newspapers and on employers' own websites.

In particular, jobs for clinical biochemists are advertised on the NHS website www.jobs.nhs.uk, and in *ACB News*, the monthly journal from the Association of Clinical Biochemistry. Trainee clinical biochemist posts are administered by the Recruitment Centre for Clinical Scientists.

While at university, or as a recent graduate, you can access information about potential employers and current graduate vacancies through your university careers service. Further information about the help available through university careers services is provided in Chapter three.

Sources of further information

Association for Clinical Biochemistry – tel: 020 7403 8001. www.acb.org.uk

Biochemical Society – tel: 020 7685 2400. www.biochemistry.org

The Institute of Science & Technology – tel: 0114 276 3197. www.istonline.org.uk

Recruitment Centre for Clinical Scientists – tel: 0871 433 3070. www.nhsclinicalscientists.info

Biotechnologist

As the name implies, the work of a biotechnologist links 'bio' (living things) with technology (the use of tools and techniques). They are concerned with how living micro-organisms can be used in industrial, medical and environmental processes – for example, in the creation of energy, the manufacture of various products and the disposal of waste. Through advances in microbiology and genetic engineering, many new ways of using micro-organisms have been developed – biotechnology is now a key industrial process in many different sectors, including those listed below.

Within the **healthcare** sector, biotechnology is used in immunology, for the production of vaccines, antibodies and antitoxins; in endocrinology, for the artificial production of hormones and other proteins; in neurobiology; in the detection of gene mutations which cause serious diseases such as cystic fibrosis, and in other diagnostic tests.

Good examples of how micro-organisms can be used in **food and drink** production include the use of yeast in bread making and brewing; while cheese, yoghurts and other dairy products also rely on microbes for their manufacture. Biotechnologists working in this sector may, for example, research and develop new dairy-type products, or artificially-produced food substitutes, flavourings and preservatives.

Within **manufacturing industries**, biotechnologists help develop those products that incorporate biological processes either in their manufacture or end use, including items such as biological washing powders, biofuels, paper and foam rubber.

Biotechnologists working in **agriculture** are concerned with increasing and improving food and animal feed production, through the development of naturally-occurring pest and disease resistance.

There are also opportunities for biotechnologists working in **environmental sectors** – in waste reclamation and recycling; the development of alternative energy sources; the manufacture of biodegradable plastics; and in pollution control, particularly relating to environmental disasters such as major oil spills.

Entry qualifications

Degrees in biotechnology vary in their content and emphasis, so research carefully which one suits your interests. However, it is not essential to take a specialist biotechnology degree to start a biotechnology career. For example, degrees in chemical engineering, biochemistry, genetics, microbiology, immunology or molecular biology can be just as suitable.

You need to be interested in practical techniques and problem solving for this type of work. Numeracy and IT skills are also important, as are an accurate and methodical approach to your work.

Training and career development

On-the-job training may involve learning about specialist equipment and computer software, as well as health and safety aspects. You may also need to attend conferences to keep up to date with developments in this field and short courses to learn about other topics, such as specific research techniques. Once in employment, it may be possible to study for a postgraduate qualification on a part-time basis. A higher degree, such as a PhD or MSc in biotechnology, may be beneficial for career progression.

Finding vacancies

Vacancies may be advertised in journals such as *New Scientist* and *Nature*, and their associated websites, by specialist recruitment agencies, on specialist online job sites, in the appointments sections of certain daily newspapers and on employers' own websites.

While at university, or as a recent graduate, you can access information about potential employers and current graduate vacancies through your university careers service. Further information about the help available through university careers services is provided in Chapter three.

Sources of further information

BioIndustry Association – tel: 020 7565 7190. www.bioindustry.org

Biotechnology and Biological Sciences Research Council – tel: 01793 413200. www.bbsrc.ac.uk

Society of Biology – tel: 020 7936 5900. www.societyofbiology.org

Botanist/Plant scientist

Botanists (also known as plant scientists) study plants, fungi and algae – their structure, how they grow and reproduce, their distribution and the diseases and pests that can affect them. The work of botanists is used in conservation, medicine and agriculture.

Some botanists concentrate on studying populations of an individual species or plant family in particular habitats – such as meadows, chalk uplands, moorland heath etc. Population studies, repeated regularly at a number of sites throughout the country, give useful information about the effects of pollution, forest fires, drought, overgrazing and so on. Botanists with specialist knowledge may perform such studies in different regions of the world. Many of the tasks of a botanist are conducted in a laboratory; one fieldwork trip can generate a great deal of follow-up lab work.

Some botanists specialise in the structure and functioning of plants. They may work in a plant-breeding station, where the size of leaf, standard height of a stem, the size of seeds or colour of petals, for example, can all be changed through breeding new hybrids that are more successful commercially. Rose breeding is one example.

Some botanists work entirely in the area of plant reproduction and genetics. This is particularly important in the development of commercially-grown crops. The control of pests is also an important aspect of botanical research.

There is considerable investigative work performed on plant nutrition, plant hormones and plant biochemistry in general. Here, botanists make use of the most advanced methods of experimentation and analysis, using sophisticated instruments, such as scanning electron microscopes and atomic absorption spectrophotometers.

The main opportunities are in government-funded research institutes and in agricultural and horticultural firms' research and development departments. Other employers include botanic gardens, such as the Royal Botanic Garden Kew, in Surrey. Research and lecturing posts in higher education are a possibility. There may be opportunities to work abroad, especially with commercial growers.

Entry qualifications

You can study plant science or botany as a single degree subject or as part of a biology degree. Opting for an applied subject, such as crop science, may help when it comes to finding work in commercial settings. Many graduates take a postgraduate course in a specialist field to improve their prospects and, if your aim is research work, a higher degree is usually a prerequisite.

Numeracy and IT skills are important for this area of work, and you will need to be able to use sophisticated equipment and scientific techniques. Botanists need to be very observant, good at problem solving and methodical in their work.

Training and career development

On-the-job training may involve learning about specialist equipment and computer software. You may also need to attend conferences to keep up to date with developments in this field and short courses to learn about other topics, such as specific research techniques. Once in employment, it may be possible to study for a postgraduate qualification on a part-time basis. A higher degree, such as a PhD or MSc may be beneficial for career progression.

Finding vacancies

Vacancies may be advertised in journals such as *New Scientist* and *Nature*, and their associated websites, by specialist recruitment agencies, on specialist online job sites, in the appointments sections of certain daily newspapers and on employers' own websites.

While at university, or as a recent graduate, you can access information about potential employers and current graduate vacancies through your university careers service. Further information about the help available through university careers services is provided in Chapter three.

Sources of further information

Botanical Society of the British Isles - www.bsbi.org.uk

Society of Biology - tel: 020 7936 5900. www.societyofbiology.org

Clinical perfusion scientist

Clinical perfusion scientists work in operating theatres managing the heart-lung machines that take over the functions of the heart and lungs during open heart surgery. They are an important part of the surgical team, making sure that the patient's organs and tissues are being adequately supplied with oxygenated blood during the operation.

Operations that clinical perfusion scientists are involved in range from the replacement of a heart valve through to heart or heart-lung transplants. In recent years, as new techniques have been developed, the role of clinical perfusion scientist has been extended to involve other procedures, such as liver transplants and the treatment of malignant skin cancers in certain parts of the body.

As a clinical perfusion scientist, you would be expected to occasionally work 'on call' in order to cover emergency and out-of-hours operations.

There are opportunities to work both in the NHS and the private sector. The Society of Clinical Perfusion Scientists of Great Britain and Ireland publishes a list of perfusion units on its website, which includes around 40 based in NHS hospitals and several operating in the private sector.

Entry qualifications

To begin training as a clinical perfusion scientist, you need a degree or postgraduate degree in a relevant scientific subject, such as biology, biomedical science, medicine, dentistry or veterinary science. Graduates of chemical or physical sciences may be accepted for entry if they have relevant clinical experience.

You need good communication skills and to be able to work well in a team and keep accurate records. It is obviously important that you are responsible and careful, and able to put patients at their ease.

Training and career development

Once employed as a trainee clinical perfusion scientist, you undergo practical training in a cardiac surgery unit, while also studying for a postgraduate qualification on a block-release basis at the North East Surrey College of Technology (NESCOT). On completion of the NESCOT course, you need to pass the professional accreditation examination of the Society of Clinical Perfusion Scientists of Great Britain and Ireland before you can begin working independently.

Promotion to senior positions may be possible following further training, advanced qualifications and involvement in clinical research work.

Finding vacancies

Trainee posts in the NHS are advertised on www.jobs.nhs.uk and within local newspapers and job centres. Some vacancies are advertised in the journal *New Scientist*, and its associated website. The Society of Clinical Perfusion Scientists of Great Britain and Ireland carries vacancies on its website and in its journal *Perfusionist*, which is free to members of the Society.

While at university, or as a recent graduate, you can access information about potential employers and current graduate vacancies through your university careers service. Further information about the help available through university careers services is provided in Chapter three.

Sources of further information

NHS Careers – tel: 0345 6060 655. www.nhscareers.nhs.uk

NHS Wales Careers – tel: 01443 233472. www.nhswalescareers.com

North East Surrey College of Technology (NESCOT) – tel: 020 8394 3038. www.nescot.ac.uk

Society of Clinical Perfusion Scientists of Great Britain and Ireland – tel: 020 7869 6891. www.scps.org.uk

Clinical scientist

Clinical scientists are trained to interpret the results of clinical tests. Their work involves helping doctors make diagnoses and monitor the effectiveness of a patient's treatment, and may involve direct patient contact. Through research, they also further our understanding of diseases and devise new therapies. Most opportunities are with NHS hospital laboratories or in community settings; other employers include organisations such as the Health Protection Agency and NHSBT (the NHS blood and transplant service).

The title of clinical scientist is protected by law, and refers to those scientists who have registered with the Health Professions Council (HPC) to work in one of the following areas, known as modalities:

- **audiology** – identifying and diagnosing hearing loss, balance disorders and neurological diseases

- **clinical biochemistry** – performing chemical and biochemical analysis on blood and other body fluids and, increasingly, working in population-screening programmes

- **embryology** – investigating infertility problems and researching IVF treatments and other forms of assisted reproduction

- **clinical genetics** – examining chromosomes and DNA to identify carriers of genetic disorders or to diagnose foetal abnormalities in pre-natal tests

- **clinical immunology** – researching the immune system and associated diseases or conditions, such as AIDS, asthma and leukaemia

- **clinical microbiology** – identifying bacterial, viral, fungal and parasitic infections

- **haematology** – investigating disorders of the blood and blood-forming tissues

- **histocompatibility & immunogenetics** – investigating the genetic factors that determine whether transplanted organs will be accepted or rejected and testing for the optimum match between donors and patients, also researching reactions to blood transfusions

- **medical physics & clinical engineering** – developing new methods of diagnosing and treating diseases, or of measuring how the body is functioning, using techniques such as ultrasound, radiation or magnetic resonance. *The work of medical physicists is described in further detail later in this chapter.*

There are only around 4,500 registered clinical scientists in the country and competition for trainee posts is intense.

Entry qualifications

To train as a clinical scientist, you need to have studied a relevant subject and gained either a first or upper second class degree, or an MSc or PhD. Postgraduate qualifications may help develop your research skills and subject knowledge and therefore give you an edge when you apply for a trainee post; however, they do not shorten the amount of time you need to spend on a pre-qualification training scheme.

Degree subjects that are considered relevant vary depending in which area of clinical science you wish to specialise. For example, a physics degree would be appropriate to train in medical physics, audiology or neurophysiology, but not haematology. In general, degrees in the life sciences – biology, microbiology, genetics or biochemistry, are most accepted. Whichever science subject you have at degree level, you will need to have basic laboratory skills, an understanding of health and safety, and knowledge of relevant terminology.

Clinical scientists need the ability to communicate with all types of people and the ability to work as part of a multi-professional team. As with other health-related careers, clinical scientists need empathy and a caring manner when dealing with patients. Manual dexterity and an analytical approach are also required.

Training and career development

In general, training involves a four-year programme leading to a Certificate of Attainment, awarded by the Association of Clinical Scientists (ACS). Gaining the Certificate is the only approved route to registration with the HPC. The training programme combines work experience in an accredited training hospital, secondments to other clinical centres and academic study, usually leading to an MSc.

Once qualified, clinical scientists can pursue higher qualifications, such as the examinations leading to Fellowship of the Royal College of Pathologists (a qualification required for consultant posts). Training is ongoing throughout your career through continuing professional development (CPD). Clinical scientists can progress to managerial positions within the health service, for example as a consultant clinical scientist.

N.B. Training programmes and career structures for clinical scientists are currently being revised, as part of the Modernising Scientific Careers programme. Changes will be implemented over the course of a few years, starting from 2010. Check the Recruitment Centre for Clinical Scientists website (listed below) for up-to-date information.

Finding vacancies

Hospitals advertise their vacancies for training positions in late November/December each year, with successful applicants commencing their employment in the following October. Undergraduates can apply during their final year of studies, provided they expect to achieve the first or upper second class degree required for entry.

Posts for trainees are advertised on the NHS Jobs website, in journals such as *New Scientist*, in the national press, via some of the professional bodies listed below or on the Recruitment Centre for Clinical Scientists website.

While at university, or as a recent graduate, you can access information about potential employers and current graduate vacancies through your university careers service. Further information about the help available through university careers services is provided in Chapter three.

Sources of further information

The Association for Clinical Biochemistry – includes a special interest group for immunology. Tel: 020 7403 8001. www.acb.org.uk

Association of Clinical Cytogenetics – 01865 226001. www.cytogenetics.org.uk

The Association of Clinical Embryologists – www.embryologists.org.uk

Association of Clinical Microbiology – www.aclinmicrobiol.org.uk

Association of Clinical Pathologists – tel: 01273 775700. www.pathologists.org.uk

British Academy of Audiology – 01625 504066. www.baaudiology.org

The British Society for Haematology – tel: 020 7713 0990. www.b-s-h.org.uk

British Society for Haemostasis and Thrombosis – www.bsht.org.uk

British Society for Histocompatibility & Imnmunogenetics – www.bshi.org.uk

British Society for Immunology – tel: 020 3031 9800. www.immunology.org

Clinical Molecular Genetics Society - www.cmgs.org

Health Professions Council (HPC) - tel: 020 7582 0866. www.hpc-uk.org

NHS Careers - tel: 0345 60 60 655. www.nhscareers.nhs.uk

NHS Wales Careers - tel: 01443 233472. www.nhswalescareers.com

Recruitment Centre for Clinical Scientists - for detailed information about training schemes and vacancies. Tel: 0871 433 3070. www.nhsclinicalscientists.info

The Royal College of Pathologists - tel: 020 7451 6700. www.rcpath.org

www.jobs.nhs.uk - the job vacancy website for NHS employers across England and Wales

Colour technologist

Colour technology is concerned with the science and technology of creating, specifying and controlling the way colour is used. It has applications in manufacturing industries, digital imaging, healthcare and communication technology, among other sectors. There are many obvious example of how colours, in the form of natural or synthetic dyes and pigments, are used in foods, cosmetics, textiles, paints, plastics, printing and so on. However, more 'high-tech' applications of colour include electronic displays, inkjet printers, lasers and medical dyes.

The work involves understanding, for example, how colours can be created so that they precisely match requirements in terms of hue, gloss, translucency and texture; are colourfast under a variety of conditions; have a minimal impact on the environment, and are safe to use. While much of the work draws on an understanding of chemistry, there are aspects relating to physics, psychology and design.

As well as roles relating to research and development, colour technologists may also be employed in technical sales and services teams - promoting colourants to commercial customers and dealing with technical queries and problems; developing processes for mass production of either colourants or end-products; and quality monitoring etc.

Entry qualifications

Currently, only the University of Leeds offers a specific degree in this area: chemistry with colour science. Degrees in chemistry (including applied or analytical chemistry), applied physics, chemical engineering, and production/manufacturing engineering may also be accepted for entry. There are a few relevant postgraduate courses if you wish to specialise in this area, again the University of Leeds is a major provider.

Obviously for this type of work you need excellent colour vision, as well as analytical and technical skills. Teamwork is important, as is commercial understanding.

Training and career development

The Society of Dyers and Colourists (SDC) offers degree-level professional qualifications that, at Associateship level, can lead to Chartered Colourist status. The Society also runs short courses, workshops, conferences and so on.

With experience, it may be possible to work as a consultant, possibly on a self-employed basis. Other routes for progression are usually into management – in areas such as production, sales, marketing, or research and development.

Finding vacancies

Vacancies may be advertised in journals such as *New Scientist* and *Chemistry World* and their associated websites, on specialist online job sites, in the appointments sections of certain daily newspapers and on employers' own websites. The SDC also advertises vacancies on its website, www.colourclick.org.

While at university, or as a recent graduate, you can access information about potential employers and current graduate vacancies through your university careers service. Further information about the help available through university careers services is provided in Chapter three.

Sources of further information

Institution of Chemical Engineers (IChemE) – tel: 01788 578214. www.icheme.org.

Royal Society of Chemistry – tel: 020 7437 8656. www.rsc.org.

Society of Dyers and Colourists – tel: 01274 725138. www.sdc.org.uk and www.colourclick.org.

Conservator

People involved in conserving works of art and other historical objects aim to preserve items for future generations to see and appreciate. They usually specialise in particular types of objects, such as paintings and drawings, books and manuscripts, ceramics, textiles, glass, photographs and so on. With the passage of time, items may be damaged by accidents, vandalism or amateur repairs, or they may have deteriorated due to the effects of the environment or a chemical instability in their make-up. The conservator's job is to preserve the object and protect it from future problems, but not to disguise the damage or make repairs, which would constitute restoration.

Conservators begin by thoroughly examining the object under consideration to assess its condition. They keep detailed records of its current state and the nature of the work to be undertaken. The item will then undergo the most appropriate treatment to prevent further deterioration. If necessary, the conservator will also determine the best environmental conditions for storing or displaying the item.

There are many institutions within the public sector that employ conservators, including the famous national museums and galleries such as the British Museum and the National Gallery, and also others run by local authorities, universities and trusts. Some conservators work in public record offices, county archives and libraries. They may also work with the National Trust and English Heritage, and other equivalent organisations around the UK. Public sector work is often based on temporary contracts, for example, working on a particular project.

There are also opportunities with the many private sector firms that provide conservation work for private collectors, museums, owners of historic properties and so on.

Entry qualifications

You usually need a degree and a postgraduate qualification for entry into this type of work. There are specific degree courses available in conservation; however most specialist training is at postgraduate level, for which a science degree, preferably relating to chemistry, is often accepted for entry. The Courtauld Institute of Art in London and the West Dean College in West Sussex, among other providers, offer relevant postgraduate courses. Icon, the Institute of Conservation, lists courses on its website.

Conservators obviously need to be interested in works of art and other antique pieces, as well as their history. The work takes patience and a methodical approach. Good eyesight, normal colour vision and manual dexterity are also required.

Training and career development

On-the-job training may involve learning about specialist equipment and techniques. You may also need to attend conferences to keep up to date with developments in this field and short courses to learn about other topics, such as specific objects and materials.

In the past, Icon has offered a limited number of internships that aim to provide work experience to recently qualified graduates. An extension of the scheme will be dependent on funding; contact Icon for further information. Icon also operates the 'training exchange', an online notice board for employers to advertise work-based training opportunities, as well as for potential trainees to advertise their details.

Experienced conservators can gain professional accreditation through the Professional Accreditation of Conservator-Restorers (PACR) scheme, which leads to Accredited Conservator-Restorer (ACR) status. To apply, conservators need to be a member of one of the following professional bodies: Icon, the Society of Archivists (SoA) or the British Horological Institute (BHI). Continuing professional development (CPD) is required to maintain accredited status.

With experience, conservators may consider self-employment in the private sector. This requires business skills as well as conservation expertise. In the public sector, promotion may mean stepping up into management, although career opportunities may be hard to find and involve moving between organisations. Some conservators move into educational work.

Finding vacancies

The Museums Association advertises vacancies in its monthly publication, *Museums Journal*, which is available free to members of the association, or through subscription; it also carries vacancies on its website. Eligible members of Icon can view job vacancies on the Icon website. Jobs in local authority museums and galleries are likely to be advertised in the local press and on www.LGjobs.com. Vacancies may also be advertised on online job sites, in the appointments sections of certain daily newspapers and on employers' own websites.

While at university, or as a recent graduate, you can access information about potential employers and current graduate vacancies through your university careers service. Further information about the help available through university careers services is provided in Chapter three.

Sources of further information

British Association of Paintings Conservators-Restorers – tel: 01603 516237. www.bapcr.org.uk

British Horological Institute – tel: 01636 813795. www.bhi.co.uk

Creative & Cultural Skills – the Sector Skills Council covering the industry. Tel: 020 7015 1800. www.ccskills.org.uk and www.creative-choices.co.uk

Icon (The Institute of Conservation) – tel: 0131 556 2289. www.icon.org.uk

The International Institute for Conservation of Historic and Artistic Works – tel: 020 7839 5975. www.iiconservation.org

Museums Association – tel: 020 7426 6910. www.museumsassociation.org

Society of Archivists – tel: 01823 327030. www.archives.org.uk Note that from 1st June, 2010, the Society of Archivists merged with the National Council of Archives and the Association of Chief Archivists in Local Government to form a new organisation, the **Archives and Records Association (UK and Ireland)**.

The Society of Bookbinders – www.societyofbookbinders.com

Worshipful Company of Glaziers & Painters of Glass – tel: 020 7403 6652. www.worshipfulglaziers.com

Consumer scientist

Many different types of job, in many different industries and organisations, fall under the realm of consumer science. In simple terms, the role of a consumer scientist is to help producers understand and meet the needs of consumers, regarding food products, fashion and textile, domestic equipment and appliances and so on.

There are opportunities to work in a variety of different specialisms. Consumer scientists working for manufacturers in **product design and development**, for example, may be part of a team of product designers, marketing staff, technologists and other scientists. They may be involved in testing products in laboratories, as well as consumer research using focus groups, tastings and interviews. Alternatively, consumer scientists may be involved in **marketing and promoting** products – liaising with reviewing journalists or organising promotional events.

Another area of work is within **consumer advisory services** – in particular, giving advice to consumers who have complaints about products. There are opportunities with local authority consumer advice centres, trading standards departments, the Food Standards Agency, or with customer relations departments of the manufacturers themselves. Within the **media**, consumer science journalists may work on TV or radio, on publications aimed at a general readership, or on professional or technical journals.

Entry qualifications

There are no specific qualifications required for work as a consumer scientist; degrees and postgraduate qualifications in a variety of subjects may be accepted by employers. Relevant subjects include food science, food and nutrition, microbiology and applied sciences, particularly applied biology or applied chemistry.

Good communication skills are required as the work involves dealing with a wide range of people at all levels. Consumer scientists also need excellent research and problem solving skills.

Training and career development

On-the-job training may involve learning about specialist equipment and research techniques. You may also need to attend conferences and exhibitions to keep up to date with developments in this field and short courses to learn about other topics, such as consumer protection laws. Once in employment, it may be possible to study for a postgraduate qualification on a part-time basis. A higher degree, such as a PhD or MSc, may be beneficial for career progression.

Finding vacancies

Vacancies may be advertised in journals such as *New Scientist, Food Manufacture* and *The Grocer* and their associated websites, by specialist recruitment agencies, on specialist online job sites, in the appointments sections of certain daily newspapers and on employers' own websites.

While at university, or as a recent graduate, you can access information about potential employers and current graduate vacancies through your university careers service. Further information about the help available through university careers services is provided in Chapter three.

Sources of further information

Food Standards Agency – tel: 020 7276 8000. www.food.gov.uk

Improve Ltd – the Sector Skills Council covering the food and drink industry. Tel: 0845 644 0448. www.improveltd.co.uk and www.improve-skills.co.uk

Institute of Food Research – tel: 01603 255000. www.ifr.ac.uk

Institute of Food Science & Technology (IFST) – tel: 020 7603 6316. www.ifst.org and www.foodtechcareers.org

Trading Standards Institute – tel: 0845 404 0506. www.tradingstandards.gov.uk

Cosmetic scientist

There are five main types of cosmetic products: perfumes and fragrances; decorative cosmetics (e.g. make-up); skin care; hair care; and toiletries. Many modern cosmetic products make great claims about their scientific credentials – anti-aging skin creams and serums packed with antioxidants, shampoos with light-reflecting agents to make hair appear more glossy, foundations containing UV filters to protect skin from sun damage and so on!

Cosmetic manufacturers, operating in highly competitive markets, rely on constant innovation to succeed. Long before a manufacturer launches a new beauty product on the market, cosmetic scientists will have played a major part in its development and manufacture. The work involves researching the safety and effectiveness of a product's individual ingredients and overall formulation, designing appropriate types of packaging to protect products from contamination and deterioration, developing processes for mass-producing products, overseeing quality control during manufacture and making sure products comply with all relevant regulations.

Even products that market themselves to appear more 'natural' will have involved a cosmetic scientist in their development, as the cosmetics industry is highly regulated in order to protect consumers. All cosmetic products must undergo a safety assessment before they can be sold to the public. In the UK, that assessment must be undertaken by a suitably qualified assessor, such as a pharmacist, chartered biologist or chartered chemist.

Entry qualifications

There are no specific qualifications required for work as a cosmetic scientist; degrees and postgraduate qualifications in a variety of subjects may be accepted by employers. Relevant subjects include biology, microbiology, chemistry, biochemistry, chemical engineering, pharmacology and cosmetic science – although, currently only a handful of institutions offer this as a degree subject.

Cosmetic scientists need excellent research and problem solving skills, as well as practical laboratory skills. Accuracy and the ability to work methodically and pay good attention to detail are also important. Developing new products requires team work and the ability to meet deadlines.

Training and career development

On-the-job training may involve learning about specific research and laboratory techniques. You may also need to attend conferences and exhibitions to keep up to date with developments in this field and short courses to learn about other topics, such as industry regulations. The Society of Cosmetic Scientists runs events and courses aimed at recent recruits to the industry as well as for those looking to progress in their careers. It may be possible to study for a postgraduate qualification on a part-time basis, while in employment.

Cosmetic scientists can develop their careers by moving into team leader or managerial positions. Scientists may be able to transfer into manufacturing, marketing, brand management or customer relations departments within their organisation.

As a member of the Royal Society of Chemistry (RSC), it is possible to work towards chartered chemist status (CChem). This requires an RSC-accredited degree or equivalent in the first instance. Similarly, as a member of the Society of Biology, it is possible to gain chartered biologist status (CBiol). This involves undertaking at least three years' postgraduate experience after gaining a degree in a bioscience, followed by a further two years' continuing professional development (CPD).

Finding vacancies

Vacancies may be advertised in journals such as *New Scientist* and *SPC* (Soap, Perfumery and Cosmetics) and their associated websites, such as the *SPC*'s www.cosmeticsbusiness.com. Jobs may also be advertised by specialist recruitment agencies, specialist online job sites, in the appointments sections of certain daily newspapers and on employers' own websites.

While at university, or as a recent graduate, you can access information about potential employers and current graduate vacancies through your university careers service. Further information about the help available through university careers services is provided in Chapter three.

Sources of further information

Cosmetic Toiletry & Perfumery Association (CTPA) – tel: 020 7491 8891. www.ctpa.org.uk

Royal Society of Chemistry – tel: 020 7437 8656. www.rsc.org

Society of Biology – tel: 020 7936 5900. www.societyofbiology.org

Society of Cosmetic Scientists – tel: 01582 726661. www.scs.org.uk

Environmental health practitioner

Environmental health practitioners (EHPs) are employed by both public and private organisations to protect the public from environmental hazards at home, in the workplace and in public spaces. For example, they may be involved in monitoring water, air, noise or land pollution, or investigating outbreaks of infectious diseases. The work may also involve checking standards of hygiene in the handling, production and storage of food, as well as inspecting food to ensure it is fit to eat. They may be involved with controlling pests such as rats, mice and insects, or with maintaining standards in the collection and disposal of refuse. Other aspects of their work include checking health and safety in shops, offices and other business premises and inspecting homes and caravan sites to ensure they are fit for habitation.

Most EHPs work for local authorities, where the exact nature of the role may vary according to geographic location – an EHP working in an area of heavy industry will deal with very different problems from someone working in a rural location. There are also opportunities in central government departments and agencies, private consultancies, industry (particularly with food manufacturers and retailers) and the armed forces. EHPs may be known as environmental health advisers or consultants, especially in the private sector.

It is possible to work as a generalist, covering many different aspects of the work, but there are also opportunities to specialise in a particular area such as environmental protection, housing, health and safety at work, food safety or public health. While the job usually involves working standard office hours, there may be some weekend and night-time working, dealing with problems as they occur. Much of the work involves being out and about, visiting a variety of different premises and locations. On occasion, EHPs may be required to give evidence at legal hearings.

The role of environmental health technician is a lower level role that, although not usually requiring a degree for entry, is often undertaken by graduates, particularly of scientific disciplines.

Entry qualifications

The first step to qualifying as an EHP is to follow a course accredited by the Chartered Institute of Environmental Health (CIEH). Accredited degrees in environmental health are available. Accredited postgraduate courses are also available, and require a science degree for entry. Some employers offer sponsorship for accredited courses, although opportunities may be limited and particularly targeted at current employees working at technician level.

Good communication skills are essential, as is the ability to get on with people from all walks of life. EHPs need to be approachable and flexible, but at the same time assertive and persuasive. They also need to be able to deal with unpleasant, possibly distressing, situations. Report writing and problem solving skills are also important.

Training and career development

As well as undertaking an accredited course, EHPs need to complete a period of work-based learning, complete a portfolio and pass professional exams in order to fully qualify. During their careers, EHPs are expected to undertake continuing professional development (CPD) and, for career progression, it may be beneficial to gain chartered status; contact the CIEH for details.

Generalist EHPs can look to specialise at any time during their careers. With experience and appropriate business skills, it may be possible to work as a consultant, perhaps on a self-employed basis.

Finding vacancies

Local authority vacancies are advertised on www.LGjobs.com. Jobs are also advertised in the CIEH journal *Environmental Health News* and its associated jobs website, www.ehn-jobs.com. Employers may also advertise vacancies on their own websites, in the appointments sections of certain daily newspapers or through specialist recruitment agencies and online job sites.

While at university, or as a recent graduate, you can access information about potential employers and current graduate vacancies through your university careers service. Further information about the help available through university careers services is provided in Chapter three.

Sources of further information

Chartered Institute of Environmental Health (CIEH) – tel: 020 7928 6006. www.cieh.org

Environmental scientist

Increasing numbers of people are taking an interest in environmental matters. Issues such as climate change, sustainable development, the destruction of rainforests and the potential extinction of certain species are becoming more widely understood and of greater concern to the general public and to many governments worldwide. Greater public awareness together with increased government investment means that job opportunities in the environmental sector look set to increase.

Opportunities in the environmental sector vary greatly. Depending on your specialism and particular interests, you could find work in the following broad areas.

- **Scientific research** – in universities and research institutes, investigating topics such as habitat restoration, renewable energy resources, air pollution etc.

- **Ecological consultancy** – advising on proposed building/ commercial developments etc by undertaking field surveys and species assessments, interpreting results and writing reports, and by applying your knowledge of protected species and environmental laws.

- **Industry and commerce** – taking responsibility for energy efficiency, waste management, reducing packaging, green supply chains and so on.

- **Government agencies** – such as the Environment Agency and Natural England, enforcing regulations, protecting and improving local environments, working with other interested parties – such as farmers and businesses, undertaking fieldwork etc.

- **Local government** – promoting recycling; monitoring pollution; assessing the environmental impacts relating to planning applications, recreation issues, and public rights of way; etc.

- **Independent organisations** – such as environmental pressure groups, conservation charities, and the National Trust, doing practical conservation, undertaking research, lobbying parliament, educating and informing etc.

- **The media** – opportunities for researchers and journalists specialising in environmental matters exist in TV, radio and in traditional and online publishing.

- **Education** – in universities and training organisations.

While some jobs in the environmental sector are very competitive to enter, in other areas there is a shortage of applicants with the necessary skills, such as taxonomy (species identification and classification) and field survey work. As a graduate, your role may be hands-on and practical, or you may manage and advise on environmental activities, either directly as an employee of the organisation or through consultancy work.

Entry qualifications

There are many degree subjects that can lead into environmental work. If you have yet to choose your degree, look carefully into the options available to you to make sure you know where they could lead. Specialised academic courses may appeal if you already have specific interests – such as in oceanography, biodiversity and conservation, environmental science and ecology. General subjects, such as in the biological, chemical and physical sciences, offer a starting point and, combined with a postgraduate qualification, will keep your options open.

Most jobs require a proven interest in the environment, and may ask for evidence of your commitment and experience, such as through part-time or voluntary work, for example. Good communication and problem solving skills are also likely to be required.

Training and career development

Training will vary according to the exact nature of your role. You may need to attend conferences to keep up to date with developments in this sector and short courses to learn about other topics. It may be possible to undertake a postgraduate qualification such as a masters degree, or even a PhD, on a part-time basis while in employment. A postgraduate qualification may be required for more senior posts.

Suitably experienced environmental professionals can gain chartered environmentalist status (CEnv), based on their knowledge, experience and other factors. Contact the Society for the Environment for full details.

Finding vacancies

Adverts for jobs appear in journals such as *New Scientist, Nature, The Environment Post*, and *The Environmentalist*, and on their associated websites. Vacancies are also advertised by specialist recruitment agencies, specialist online job sites, some of the professional bodies listed below, in the appointments sections of certain daily newspapers (such as Wednesday's *Guardian*) and on employers' own websites.

While at university, or as a recent graduate, you can access information about potential employers and current graduate vacancies through your university careers service. Further information about the help available through university careers services is provided in Chapter three.

Sources of further information

British Ecological Society – tel: 020 685 2500.
www.britishecologicalsociety.org

The Chartered Institution of Water and Environmental Management – tel: 020 7831 3110. www.ciwem.org and www.environmentalcareers.org.uk

Countryside Council for Wales – tel: 0845 130 6229. www.ccw.gov.uk

Countryside Jobs Service – issues a weekly listing of countryside jobs – *CJS Weekly*. A two- to 10-week online subscription costs £1.65 per week. Samples of the weekly jobs list can be found on the website. Tel: 01947 896007. www.countryside-jobs.com

Environment Agency – tel: 08708 506506.
www.environment-agency.gov.uk

Institute of Ecology and Environmental Management – tel: 01962 868626. www.ieem.net

Institute of Environmental Management & Assessment – tel: 01522 540069. www.iema.net

The Institution of Environmental Sciences – tel: 020 7730 5516. www.ies-uk.org.uk

Lantra – the Sector Skills Council for the environmental and land-based sector. Tel: 0845 707 8007. www.lantra.co.uk and www.afuturein.com

Natural England – tel: 0845 600 3078. www.naturalengland.org.uk

Natural Environment Research Council – tel: 01793 411500. www.nerc.ac.uk

Society for the Environment – tel: 0845 337 2951. www.socenv.org.uk

The Wildlife Trusts – tel: 01636 677711. www.wildlifetrusts.org

Ergonomist

Ergonomics is about making sure that the design of objects, environments and systems takes into account human factors, so that people can work more efficiently, safely and with fewer mistakes. For example:

- objects ranging from vacuum cleaners to cars may be designed ergonomically in order to make them comfortable and instinctive to use

- equipment and workstations need to be designed to take account of differing body proportions and to avoid poor posture

- lighting and heating systems need to suit the requirements of the workers and the tasks they are undertaking

- tasks and jobs need to be planned in such a way so as to incorporate adequate rest breaks and sensible shift patterns

- user interfaces with computers and control systems need to be easy to understand and operate, particularly in safety-critical environments, such as the cockpit of an aeroplane.

The work draws on a knowledge of psychology, anatomy and physiology, as well as engineering and design. It involves understanding the tasks to be undertaken and also the users – their capabilities and their limitations.

There are opportunities for ergonomists in a wide range of industries. They may be called upon to assess workplaces, develop guidance on best practice, design new products or research user behaviour, for example. Ergonomists tend to work in teams with other professionals, such as design engineers, computer specialists, and health and safety practitioners. The work often involves visiting different sites and meeting different people, as well as report writing and working on practical solutions to problems.

Entry qualifications

To work as an ergonomist, you need a degree or postgraduate qualification in ergonomics. Postgraduate courses are open to those with a degree in psychology, biology, medicine, engineering and related subjects. Certain courses are recognised by the Ergonomics Society for membership of the Society.

Ergonomists need excellent communication skills in order to be able to explain complex ideas to non-specialists. They also require patience and good observation skills to conduct workplace assessments and similar research.

Training and career development

Training will vary depending on the exact nature of your job and the industry you are working in. It is likely to include on-the-job training and short courses. You may also need to attend exhibitions to keep up to date with developments in this field. It may be possible to study for a postgraduate qualification on a part-time basis, while in employment.

Progression may be to a supervisory or senior management position, or by specialising in a particular branch of ergonomics. With experience, it may be possible to work as a consultant, perhaps on a self-employed basis if you have the necessary business skills.

Finding vacancies

Vacancies are advertised in the Ergonomics Society's monthly newsletter, The Ergonomist (available free to members) and on the Society's website (access restricted to members only). Jobs are also advertised by specialist recruitment agencies, specialist online job sites, in the appointments sections of certain daily newspapers and on employers' own websites.

While at university, or as a recent graduate, you can access information about potential employers and current graduate vacancies through your university careers service. Further information about the help available through university careers services is provided in Chapter three.

Sources of further information

The Ergonomics Society – tel: 01509 234904. www.ergonomics.org.uk

Food scientist/technologist

The food and drink industry is big business in the UK. Many different producers and manufacturers are involved in the complex supply chain that leads from raw ingredients to the meal on your plate. We are fortunate in this country to have access to a wide variety of fresh and processed products – which, to a large degree, is due to the work of food scientists and technologists.

Food scientists and technologist are behind the various types of handling, processing and storage techniques that are involved in food manufacture and production. Our food and drink choices would be severely limited if it.were not for those items that have been frozen, chilled, freeze dried, baked, canned or bottled at some stage in their production.

Food scientists and technologists are also involved in developing new or improved products to meet changing consumer demands. As with many other aspects of our lives, our tastes in food and drink are influenced by fads and fashion, but other factors, such as health concerns, environmental issues and income also affect our eating and drinking habits. Manufacturers rely on food scientists and technologists to find new ways of responding to these pressures – for example, by reducing the salt and fat content of products without compromising on taste, finding ways to extend the shelf-life of items, improving flavours and developing new products.

There are opportunities to specialise in the food and drink sector in the following areas:

- **food science** – the study of the biology, physics and chemistry of foods, at every stage from raw material, through processing, to the finished product
- **food technology** – finding practical applications of the science
- **food microbiology** – concerning safe food supplies

- **food engineering** – including the design and maintenance of the equipment used in large-scale food production.

Opportunities exist with manufacturers and producers in research and development, quality assurance, production and management. Food scientists and technologists are also employed by food retailers, independent research and consultancy companies, packaging manufacturers and in local government and other statutory departments, such as environmental health, trading standards, the Food Standards Agency, Defra (the Department for Environment, Food and Rural Affairs) and the Department of Health.

Entry qualifications

Most food scientists and technologists qualify by taking a degree course in food science, food technology or a closely-related discipline. Entry to this area of work is also open to graduates of other relevant subjects, including chemistry, physics, biochemistry, microbiology, biotechnology and engineering, who could consider taking a relevant postgraduate course or may be offered specific training once in employment.

For this type of work, you need to be organised, methodical and a good team worker. You also need analytical skills and the ability to work under pressure. A strong commitment to health and safety, as well as hygiene, is also important.

Training and career development

Training is likely to be on the job and you may be expected to attend short courses and industry events in order to keep up to date with developments in this field. It may be possible to study for a postgraduate qualification on a part-time basis, while in employment. Some large food companies offer graduate training schemes.

Progression may be to a supervisory or senior management position, or by specialising in a particular market sector or technology. With experience, it may be possible to work as a consultant, perhaps on a self-employed basis if you have the necessary business skills.

Finding vacancies

Vacancies may be advertised in journals such as *New Scientist* and *Food Manufacture*, and on their associated websites. Jobs are also advertised by specialist recruitment agencies, specialist online job sites, in the appointments sections of certain daily newspapers and on employers' own websites.

While at university, or as a recent graduate, you can access information about potential employers and current graduate vacancies through your university careers service. Further information about the help available through university careers services is provided in Chapter three.

Sources of further information

Food and Drink Federation – tel: 020 7836 2460. www.fdf.org.uk

Institute of Food Science & Technology – tel: 020 7603 6316. www.ifst.org and www.foodtechcareers.org

Improve Ltd – the Sector Skills Council for the food and drink industry. Tel: 0845 644 0448. www.improveltd.co.uk and www.improve-skills.co.uk/careers

Forensic scientist

Forensic scientists work closely with the police, and others, to provide impartial, scientific evidence for use in courts of law. They analyse many different types of physical evidence to help establish whether a crime has been committed, and if so, to help solve that crime. Forensic scientists use various tests to analyse materials from the scene of a crime, a victim or a weapon, for example. Their findings may be used to link a person to the crime, or help eliminate a suspect from the enquiry. Forensic scientists also work on civil cases, such as DNA testing in paternity cases and so on.

There is a range of scientific techniques employed by forensic scientists. For example, tests can identify the presence and distribution of blood, hair, body tissue and fluids, as well as fibres from clothing. DNA evidence can be profiled and compared to the National DNA Database to search for a match. Tyre marks, foot prints and handwriting can be analysed, as can traces of paint, explosives, drugs and poisons.

The work may involve helping police investigate all manner of incidents, including explosions, suspected arson, murders and road accidents. It may be necessary to visit the scene of the incident to collect material to be analysed, although this is more often done by police scenes of crime officers. Much of the work is undertaken in a laboratory using specialised equipment and techniques, such as microscopy, spectroscopy, radiography and chromatography. Digital forensics is a developing area that involves the technical examination of computers, mobile phones and other modern technology for evidence. Forensic scientists tend to specialise in a particular area of the work.

The main employer for forensic scientists is the Forensic Science Service (FSS). There are also opportunities with the police in scientific support laboratories, independent forensic laboratories and universities. Many forensic scientists work as self-employed consultants.

Entry qualifications

There is tough competition for vacancies, so previous laboratory experience and a postgraduate qualification could put you at an advantage. Science graduates with at least a 2:2 degree, preferably in a chemistry- or biology-based subject, can apply for trainee forensic scientist posts with the FSS. Note that a degree in forensic science will not necessarily qualify you for the job, therefore research the science content of such courses carefully and check out the employment destinations of previous students. The Forensic Science Society (FSSoc) accredits degrees and postgraduate qualifications in forensic science and, together with Skills for Justice, has developed the Forensic Skillsmark. Visit www.skillsmark.net for further information.

To work in forensic science you need to be objective, methodical and extremely accurate. Teamwork is important, as is the ability to think independently and analytically. Good communication skills are also required – the work involves report writing and, in the case of senior scientists and reporting officers, presenting evidence in court. Some jobs require normal colour vision.

Training and career development

Training is on the job and also involves attending short courses. The FSS offers training in areas ranging from management through to ballistics and firearms. It may be possible to study for a postgraduate qualification on a part-time basis, while in employment, in forensic science or in specialist areas, such as digital forensics. With experience or postgraduate research, it's possible to gain promotion in the FSS to senior forensic scientist. FSS forensic scientists can train to work as reporting officers, who give evidence in court, either in support of the prosecution or defence.

Progression may be to a supervisory or senior management position, or by specialising in a particular market sector or technology. With experience, it may be possible to work as a consultant, perhaps on a self-employed basis if you have the necessary business skills.

Finding vacancies

The FSS advertises vacancies on its website, in the regional and national press, and in publications such as *New Scientist, Police Review* and *Chemistry World*. Other employers may advertise vacancies on their own websites, online job sites or through specialist recruitment agencies.

While at university, or as a recent graduate, you can access information about potential employers and current graduate vacancies through your university careers service. Further information about the help available through university careers services is provided in Chapter three.

Sources of further information

Forensic Science Service (FSS) – www.forensic.gov.uk

Forensic Science Society (FSSoc) – tel: 01423 506068. www.forensic-science-society.org.uk

Skills for Justice – the Sector Skills Council covering the justice sector. Tel: 0114 261 1499. www.skillsforjustice.com

Forester

The forestry industry is mainly concerned with producing timber from managed plantations. This involves growing trees from seedlings, pruning and felling trees, processing timber and transporting wood to sawmills. Forests also play an important part in wildlife conservation and are popular places for people to visit for all sorts of outdoor activities.

Foresters are the supervisors and managers in forestry. They plan annual programmes of work and oversee operations. They may keep records about the sale of timber and the purchase of materials; train and manage staff, liaise with landowners and other relevant parties, and ensure the land and trees are treated correctly.

In the UK, around 12% of the land is woodland, with major forested areas in East Anglia, the New Forest, Cumbria, Wales and Scotland. A few urban woodlands also exist. Private individuals, companies, local authorities, trusts and charities own around two-thirds of the country's forests; the rest is the responsibility of the Forestry Commission, the government department responsible for the protection and expansion of Britain's forests and woodlands.

The Forestry Commission employs foresters, known as forest officers, and also research scientists in its Forest Research Agency. Scientists may be involved in research into woodland biodiversity, climate change and protecting trees from pests and diseases, for example.

Entry qualifications

A degree in forestry or arboriculture is likely to be preferred, although it may be possible to enter employment as a forester with a degree in environmental science, ecology, horticulture or a related subject. Relevant postgraduate qualifications are available for those with a degree in biological or related sciences. The Institute of Chartered Foresters (ICF) accredits certain degrees and postgraduate qualifications.

In the past, the Forestry Commission has run a three-year Graduate Development Programme, open to graduates with at least a 2:1 degree in any subject, with the aim of developing future senior managers across the whole of the business. Visit the Forestry Commission website for information about when the programme will next run.

Foresters need an interest in environmental matters and to enjoy outdoor work. Supervisory and communication skills are important; the work also requires practical skills and the ability to manage projects. A driving licence is usually required for this type of work.

Training and career development

Employers provide their own training, which is likely to consist of practical courses and management skills training. With an ICF-accredited degree or postgraduate qualification, it is possible to work toward chartered forester status. This involves undertaking mentored work experience, a written assessment and an oral examination. Chartered Foresters must undertake continuing professional development to maintain their professional status.

Foresters may be able to develop their careers by specialising in scientific research or by moving into management. With experience, it may be possible to work as a consultant, perhaps on a self-employed basis if you have the necessary business skills.

Finding vacancies

Jobs may be advertised by specialist recruitment agencies and online job sites, in the appointments sections of certain daily newspapers and on employers' own websites. The Forestry Commission advertises its vacancies on its own website.

While at university, or as a recent graduate, you can access information about potential employers and current graduate vacancies through your university careers service. Further information about the help available through university careers services is provided in Chapter three.

Sources of further information

ConFor (Confederation of Forest Industries) – tel: 0131 240 1410. www.confor.org.uk

Countryside Jobs Service – issues a weekly listing of countryside jobs – CJS Weekly. A two- to 10-week online subscription costs £1.65 per week. Samples of the weekly jobs list can be found on the website. Tel: 01947 896007. www.countryside-jobs.com

Forestry Commission – tel: 0131 334 0303. www.forestry.gov.uk

Forestry Contracting Association – www.fcauk.com

Institute of Chartered Foresters – tel: 0131 240 1425. www.charteredforesters.org

Lantra – Sector Skills Council for the environmental and land-based sector. Tel: 0845 707 8007. www.lantra.co.uk and www.afuturein.com

National School of Forestry – tel: 01768 893621. www.cumbria.ac.uk/forestry

Royal Forestry Society – tel: 01442 822028. www.rfs.org.uk

The Woodland Trust – tel: 01476 581135. www.woodlandtrust.org.uk

Geoscientist

Geoscientists study the structure, evolution and composition of the earth and its natural mineral and energy resources. Geoscientists work in a range of different roles and industries. The main areas of work are outlined below.

- **Geologists** may sample rocks, analyse landslides and floods, and collect fossil and mineral specimens for analysis and identification in the laboratory. Some study the behaviour of volcanoes.

- **Geophysicists** carry out tests and large-scale surveys on the physical properties of rocks – such as magnetism, resistivity and natural radioactivity – at the earth's surface or in boreholes. Geophysicists use sensitive equipment to measure small variations in these physical properties, to reveal the types and structures of the rocks beneath the ground.

- **Geochemists** analyse rock, sediment or stream samples in the search for mineral resources of possible economic importance, or in the course of environmental assessment.

- **Hydrogeologists** use their knowledge of geological formations to study underground water and the movement and behaviour of water in aquifers (rock or soil that transmits water). They also advise on water supply and quality.

- **Environmental geoscientists** are concerned with the air, water and land on which people, plants and animals depend, and their protection from damage resulting from geological activities such as mining, oil exploration and the disposal of waste.

- **Engineering geologists** work on projects ranging from the construction of buildings, dams and tunnels or the design of mines and quarries, through to assessing the stability of slopes.

- **Seismologists** study earthquakes and their effects, such as tsunamis, in order to predict when and where they may occur.

Geoscientists present their work in the form of papers or technical reports.

The main employers of geoscientists are oil, gas, water, mining/quarrying and civil engineering companies. One of the major employers in the UK is the government-funded British Geological Survey (BGS). The BGS undertakes long-term surveying and monitoring across the UK and offshore, and provides a national geoscientific information service. It also undertakes research commissioned by others. A few posts are available in other research institutes and in research in universities.

Entry qualifications

You normally need a degree and, often, postgraduate qualifications to work as a professional geoscientist. Acceptable degree courses include geology, geoscience and earth sciences, as well as the more specialised areas of geophysics, environmental geoscience and marine geoscience. Some degree courses combine geology with related subjects, such as geography or environmental science. Many degrees are accredited by the Geological Society.

Graduates of other science disciplines may also specialise in branches of geoscience. For example, a physicist may become a geophysicist or a chemist may specialise in geochemistry; taking a postgraduate qualification may be necessary.

Geoscientists need problem solving, ICT, communication and observation skills, and the ability to work well in a team.

Training and career development

Postgraduate study is almost essential if you want to work at the highest levels. Graduates who have gained the necessary work experience, have undertaken professional development and are fellows of the Geological Society, can gain chartered geologist status (CGeol).

To gain promotion, you may have to be prepared to move. Many professional geologists spend part of their career working abroad. Some experienced geologists become self-employed consultants.

Finding vacancies

You should check the websites of companies involved in providing geoscientific services. Look at the British Geological Survey's website for current vacancies with the BGS, and at journals such as *New Scientist* and it's associated website.

While at university, or as a recent graduate, you can access information about potential employers and current graduate vacancies through your university careers service. Further information about the help available through university careers services is provided in Chapter three.

Sources of further information

British Geological Survey – tel: 0115 936 3143. www.bgs.ac.uk

The Geological Society – tel: 020 7434 9944. www.geolsoc.org.uk

Health and safety inspector

Health and safety inspectors are civil servants who work for the Health and Safety Executive (HSE), which has offices throughout the UK. Inspectors check health and safety standards in a range of areas of industry and public services, including manufacturing, construction, the railways, hospitals and utility suppliers (gas/electricity and water). They make sure that employers comply with health and safety laws, that people who work in dangerous environments are properly trained and that employees are protected from hazards such as asbestos, radioactive materials and other toxic or dangerous substances. Much of the work involves providing employers with guidance and advice. However, inspectors have to prepare evidence for prosecutions, and may be required to attend court.

The day-to-day work is a mix of visiting employers and office-based work. This includes visiting employers' premises to carry out inspections, which may involve sampling and taking readings of various environmental factors. Inspectors also investigate accidents, to find out if they have been caused by non-compliance with the law, and look into complaints of possible breaches of the law. They must keep careful records and write reports on their findings and have to decide when taking legal action is necessary. Keeping up to date with health and safety legislation is an important part of the work.

Some inspectors specialise in particular areas of industry, such as radiation protection. This is needed not only in the nuclear industry, but also in hospitals, research institutes, defence establishments etc.

The HSE operates a scientific research laboratory, based in Derbyshire. You can find out more about this through the HSE website.

A related role to health and safety inspector is that of health and safety adviser (who also may be called health and safety officer or manager). These are employed by local authorities and other large employers to ensure that their organisation complies with health and safety legislation. The role generally includes inspecting and auditing their organisation, developing policies, advising managers, staff training, undertaking risk assessments and investigating accidents. A similar role, in some respects, is that of environmental health practitioner, described earlier in this chapter.

Entry qualifications

There are no set entry requirements to train as an HSE inspector, but most entrants hold degrees. Degrees in science, technology and engineering are useful, and are required for some specialist positions, which may also need relevant work experience.

Inspectors must have good powers of observation and good communication, analytical, investigative and problem-solving skills. They have to be able to work effectively with senior managers within the organisations they are investigating and work well under pressure.

Training and career development

During their first two years, new inspectors with the HSE are trained on the job and through courses. Trainees generally work towards a work-related qualification in health and safety regulation, and training may lead to a postgraduate qualification. Inspectors need to update their knowledge continuously. With experience, promotion to more senior positions within the HSE is possible.

For those working in health and safety work generally, a range of qualifications is available, including the Level 6 Diploma in Occupational Safety and Health. See the websites of the British Safety Council, NEBOSH, and IOSH (listed below) for information on relevant qualifications.

Finding vacancies

Vacancies are posted on the HSE website, www.hse.gov.uk. Entry is competitive.

You can also view a range of vacancies in health and safety work on www.healthandsafety-jobs.co.uk. The local government vacancy website carries positions for health and safety staff within local authorities: www.LGjobs.com.

While at university, or as a recent graduate, you can access information about potential employers and current graduate vacancies through your university careers service. Further information about the help available through university careers services is provided in Chapter three.

Sources of further information

British Safety Council – tel: 020 8741 1231. www.britishsafetycouncil.co.uk

Health and Safety Executive (HSE) – tel: 0845 345 0055. www.hse.gov.uk

International Institute of Risk and Safety Management – tel: 020 8741 9100. www.iirsm.org

IOSH (Institution of Occupational Safety and Health) – tel: 0116 257 3100. www.iosh.co.uk

NEBOSH (National Examination Board in Occupational Safety and Health) – tel: 0116 263 4700. www.nebosh.org.uk

Society for Radiological Protection – tel: 01364 644487. www.srp-uk.org

Horticulturist

Horticulture is concerned with the cultivation of flowers, vegetables, fruits, and ornamental plants. Most opportunities relate to either commercial or amenity horticulture. As the name suggests, **commercial horticulture** (also known as production horticulture) involves growing plants and crops for sale – for example, selling plants through nurseries and garden centres, or fruit, vegetables and flowers through supermarkets, greengrocers and florists. **Amenity horticulture** relates to the management, design and maintenance of public and private spaces, such as parks, gardens, sports grounds, landscapes around building developments and interior landscapes (where indoor plants are incorporated as part of an enclosed environment).

Horticulture offers a variety of careers for graduates, some of which are described below.

- **Harvest/production manager** – responsible for the day-to-day running of large nurseries or horticultural businesses that supply retailers. The work may involve managing the workers involved in harvesting and packaging crops, quality assurance, planning production and managing the time-critical supply of produce to buyers.

- **Nursery manager** – responsible for managing plant nurseries that sell to the public, garden centres and other retail outlets. Tasks may include buying stock such as seeds, bulbs, fertilizer and so on; managing and training staff; monitoring the quality of stock; marketing and production management.

- **Technical sales rep** – opportunities for graduates exist across the 'agribusiness' sector selling on behalf of chemical companies that produce fertilisers, pesticides, hormone preparations etc; manufacturers of equipment and machinery; wholesale companies; etc.

- **Landscape manager** – the work involves making sure spaces, such as parks and public gardens, are carefully designed to meet the needs of visitors and other users, devising maintenance plans, managing contractors and controlling budgets.

- **Research scientist** – a range of organisations undertake research to improve crop yields, prevent plant diseases, control pests, develop new strains of plants, re-establish endangered species and so on. Potential employers include the institutes supported by the Biotechnology and Biological Sciences Research Council (BBSRC); the Royal Horticultural Society (RHS); the Royal Botanic Gardens, Kew; agrochemical companies; seed specialists and plant breeders.

- **Horticultural adviser** – either working as a self-employed consultant, or with an agency such as ADAS (the UK's largest, independent environmental consultancy), advisers provide services to commercial companies, giving technical advice and guidance on regulations etc.

- **Technical writer** – some posts are available with 'agribusiness' manufacturers and suppliers to write product information – for catalogues, websites, user guides, information leaflets and so on.

- **Horticultural therapist** – working with people who have special needs, horticulture can be used as a therapeutic activity.

Entry qualifications

Horticultural careers are open to graduates from a range of disciplines, not just those relating specifically to horticulture. Degrees in subjects such as applied science, biology, biochemistry, microbiology, chemistry, botany, environmental science and plant science are also acceptable for entry. There are some relevant postgraduate courses available, for which a science degree would be acceptable for entry.

In general, good communication and team-management skills are required for most types of horticultural work. An ability to keep pace with new developments, particularly for commercial horticulture, is also required.

Training and career development

Training will vary depending on the particular type of role undertaken, but is likely to incorporate short courses and training in the workplace. It may be possible to study part time for a postgraduate qualification while in employment.

Career development will depend on your specialism and interests. It may be possible to move into general management, consultancy work or teaching, for example.

Finding vacancies

Jobs are advertised in journals such as *Horticulture Week* and its associated website. Employers may also advertise vacancies on their own websites or through specialist recruitment agencies, online job sites and the appointments sections of certain national newspapers. Local authority vacancies are advertised on www.LGjobs.com.

While at university, or as a recent graduate, you can access information about potential employers and current graduate vacancies through your university careers service. Further information about the help available through university careers services is provided in Chapter three.

Sources of further information

ADAS - tel: 0845 766 0085. www.adas.co.uk

Biotechnology and Biological Sciences Research Council (BBSRC) - tel: 01793 413200. www.bbsrc.ac.uk

DEFRA (Department for Environment, Food and Rural Affairs) - tel: 08459 335577. www.defra.gov.uk

Fera (Food and Environment Research Agency) - tel: 01904 462000. www.fera.defra.gov.uk

Institute of Horticulture - tel: 01992 707025. www.horticulture.org.uk

Lantra - the Sector Skills Council for the environmental and land-based sector. Tel: 0845 707 8007. www.lantra.co.uk and www.afuturein.com

Royal Horticultural Society - tel: 0845 260 5000. www.rhs.org.uk

Thrive - a national charity that uses gardening to change the lives of disabled people. Contact for information on training in horticultural therapy. Tel: 0118 988 5688. www.thrive.org.uk

www.growcareers.info - a website (supported by various bodies, including Lantra) that carries information on the range of careers relating to horticulture.

Hydrologist

Hydrologists are concerned with our freshwater resources. They contribute to ensuring the continued and sustainable availability of water resources for domestic and industrial use. They get involved in planning and designing water supplies and managing and conserving water. Their work covers all freshwater systems, including rivers, lakes and reservoirs. They also need to understand groundwater systems, water movements and water catchment areas and try to predict future trends in water supply. Looking at water quality and at supplying water in the most cost effective way is an important part of the work. They investigate the effects of droughts, floods, long-term climate change and changes of land use (such as deforestation or building development) on the available water supply.

The day-to-day work of hydrologists includes fieldwork and office-based work. In the field, they may take water samples to test for quality, set up flow-measurement monitoring systems, record water levels and so on. They undertake desk-based research and analysis, using computer models to help with data interpretation and making predictions. They write reports, make recommendations on water management and give advice. They have to balance the need for environmental conservation with the demands of water for domestic use, industry and agriculture.

Hydrologists work closely with a variety of other professionals including freshwater biologists, ecologists, civil engineers and water engineers.

Hydrologists are employed by water and environmental consultancies, water companies, government bodies such as the Environment Agency, and research establishments, such as the Centre for Ecology and Hydrology (part of the Natural Environment Research Council).

Entry qualifications

Entrants normally need a relevant degree, which includes subjects such as environmental science, earth sciences, civil engineering and applied science. A relevant postgraduate qualification may be helpful or required for some positions. The Chartered Institution of Water and Environmental Management (CIWEM) accredits a small number of first degrees and many postgraduate qualifications.

Good communication skills (oral and written) are important, as are analytical, mathematical, ICT, problem solving and project management skills.

Training and career development

Training is undertaken on the job, supplemented with training courses in particular aspects of the work. Hydrologists need to keep themselves up to date with developments in their field, so need to undertake continuous professional development (CPD) and attend conferences, etc.

CIWEM offers a professional recognition scheme, and it may be possible to reach chartered status, including chartered scientist and chartered environmentalist, through a relevant professional body.

With experience, there are opportunities to work as a self-employed consultant. It is also possible to work overseas.

Finding vacancies

Vacancies are advertised on the website of the British Hydrological Society, CIWEM and the Institute of Water (see below), on www.waterjobs.co.uk and in professional journals such as *New Scientist* or *New Civil Engineer* and their associated websites.

While at university, or as a recent graduate, you can access information about potential employers and current graduate vacancies through your university careers service. Further information about the help available through university careers services is provided in Chapter three.

Sources of further information

British Hydrological Society - tel: 020 7222 7722. www.hydrology.org.uk

Chartered Institution of Water and Environmental Management (CIWEM) - tel: 020 7831 3110. www.ciwem.org

Institute of Water - tel: 0191 422 0088. www.iwo.org.uk

Industrial chemist

Industrial chemists use their chemical knowledge and expertise in industrial settings.

The term industrial chemist is broad, and includes chemists that work in research and development, production chemists, who are concerned with manufacturing processes, and chemists who work in quality control.

- Within **research and development**, the work is mainly laboratory based. Industrial chemists use their knowledge of the properties of chemicals to develop new, more efficient and effective chemical products. They also work on improving the chemical production processes. They undertake small- and large-scale trials and make reports and recommendations.

- **Production chemists** are concerned with the running of the production lines, ensuring that the manufacturing process of chemical products is efficient and cost effective. Ensuring that the production processes comply with health and safety regulations is also an area of responsibility and training of production line staff may form part of the job.

• Industrial chemists working in **quality control** are responsible for ensuring that the quality of goods being produced is maintained, through constant monitoring, testing and sampling of products against the company specifications.

Depending on their role, industrial chemists may work closely with production managers and supervisors, chemical engineers, measurement and control engineers, materials scientists and analytical chemists. They may have contact with food technologists, pharmacologists, agricultural scientists or metallurgists.

Industrial chemists are employed in a very wide range of industries. For example, manufacturers of plastics, chemicals, pharmaceuticals, paint and coatings, food and drink, cosmetics, cleaning products, building materials and agricultural materials such as fertilizers and pesticides all need the knowledge of industrial chemists. The oil and petrochemical industries are also an important employer and waste processing is a further possible area of employment. Industrial chemists may be employed within research establishments.

Entry qualifications

Industrial chemists need a chemistry-related degree. There are some chemistry degrees available with an industrial orientation, including a few that offer industrial experience as part of the course. Some entrants may have postgraduate qualifications, which are offered by some institutions in various aspects of industrial chemistry. Any prior relevant work experience is valued by employers.

Industrial chemists need good communication, analytical and problem solving skills. They need to be thorough and accurate in their approach to work, and the ability to work in a team and to work to deadlines is important.

Training and career development

Training is mainly on the job and through short courses arranged by the employer in specific aspects of the work. Industrial chemists may study for a postgraduate qualification on a part-time basis while in employment.

Industrial scientists can develop their careers by moving into team leader or managerial positions.

Finding vacancies

Employers may advertise their vacancies on their own websites, through specialist recruitment agencies, via online job sites or in the appointment sections of scientific journals.

While at university, or as a recent graduate, you can access information about potential employers and current graduate vacancies through your university careers service. Further information about the help available through university careers services is provided in Chapter three.

Sources of further information

Royal Society of Chemistry (RSC) – tel: 020 7437 8656. www.rsc.org/studentzone

Laboratory technician

Laboratory technicians assist professional scientists and technologists to carry out scientific investigations and experiments.

Laboratory technicians are involved in the routine day-to-day work in the laboratory. They make sure that stock levels are maintained, check that equipment is in perfect working order and ensure everything is clean or sterile. They may set up the equipment, prepare and help to conduct experiments, and record findings. The following are the main areas of work.

- **Industrial** – laboratory technicians work in a wide range of settings in industry. This includes companies making chemicals, pharmaceutical firms, textile factories working with dyes and fabrics, paint factories, food processing factories, the rubber and plastics industry and agricultural feed and chemical suppliers. Technicians may be employed in research and development or in quality control of products as they are manufactured.

- **Medical** – the hospital pathology laboratory is where samples such as body fluids and tissue taken from patients are tested and analysed. Medical laboratory assistants, also known as assistant practitioners (medical lab), assist qualified biomedical scientists in their work. The duties include helping prepare samples for analysis, making up solutions, sorting, checking and labelling samples, maintaining equipment stocks and so on. Technicians also work in medical research laboratories.

- **Government and local government** – a number of government agencies and government-funded research institutes employ scientific staff, including laboratory technicians. Opportunities include working in defence research, environmental research, public health and food and agricultural science. Local authorities employ laboratory technicians in environmental health and trading standards departments (and in schools – see below).

- **Educational** – technicians work in schools, colleges and universities. They are responsible for the laboratory equipment used by teaching staff and students. Laboratory technicians prepare chemicals and other materials and help to set up experiments. In higher education establishments, technicians may also assist with research.

Entry qualifications

Traditionally, entry to laboratory technician work has required a minimum of GCSEs or A level, or equivalent, qualifications. However, increasingly, successful applicants hold higher education qualifications, including science degrees. For some positions, graduates may view laboratory technician work as a route to gaining entry into the organisation, with the hope that they may move into a graduate-level position later.

Laboratory staff need to be patient, methodical and accurate workers, able to work independently and as part of a team, capable of observing strict safety procedures and, in some jobs, willing to work shifts.

Training and career development

Training is mainly on the job. It may be possible to gain work-related qualifications in the workplace. In larger laboratories, promotion to supervisor or laboratory management may be possible.

Finding vacancies

As laboratories usually employ only a small number of staff, jobs can be difficult to find. Vacancies may be advertised in local papers. You can find local authority vacancies on www. LGjobs.com.

While at university, or as a recent graduate, you can access information about potential employers and current graduate vacancies through your university careers service. Further information about the help available through university careers services is provided in Chapter three.

Sources of further information

The Institute of Science & Technology (IST) – tel: 0114 276 3197. www.istonline.org.uk

Landscape scientist

Landscape scientists are concerned with the physical and biological aspects of a designed landscape. For example, decisions about how to landscape an old industrial site or the most suitable plants to grow in a particular area often require specialist scientific knowledge, and this is where the landscape scientist comes in.

Landscape scientists work closely with landscape architects, landscape managers and contractors, planners and civil engineers. Landscaping projects may include the development of 'brown field' and 'green field' sites. Landscape scientists can be involved at all stages of a project – from initial planning through to future maintenance and management. The work may include:

- investigating the physical features of a site, such as the soil and other geographical aspects, to identify any restoration work required, and the plant species most suited to the site – particularly important where pollution may have contaminated the site

- surveying the plant and animal species of a site

- assessing and reporting on the impact of proposed building development on the wildlife, and drawing up management plans for future wildlife protection

- drawing up planting schemes and plans for creating new habitats to enhance the wildlife on the site

- managing the landscape construction of the project

- creating plans for future conservation management of the site.

Some landscape scientists specialise in particular areas of the work, such as soil science or wildlife conservation.

Most are employed by environmental and landscape consultancies. There are some opportunities within local authorities. It is also possible to work in research establishments.

Entry qualifications

To work as a landscape scientist, you usually need a degree or a postgraduate qualification accredited by the Landscape Institute (LI). Entry requirements for postgraduate qualifications vary and your first degree may need to be in a relevant subject. A list of LI-accredited courses is available on the LI website (see below).

Apart from technical and scientific knowledge, landscape scientists need good communication and negotiation skills, good organisational skills, the ability to work in a team and independently and to be prepared to travel.

Training and career development

After completing an accredited degree or postgraduate qualification, you can become a chartered member of the Landscape Institute (CMLI) by following their 'Pathway to Chartership'. This involves undertaking at least two years' practical work experience under the supervision of a mentor before taking the LI's oral exam.

Finding vacancies

Landcaping vacancies are advertised on the websites of the Landscape Institute (see below) and the British Association of Landscape Industries, www.bali.co.uk.

While at university, or as a recent graduate, you can access information about potential employers and current graduate vacancies through your university careers service. Further information about the help available through university careers services is provided in Chapter three.

Sources of further information

The Landscape Institute (LI) – tel: 020 7299 4500.
www.landscapeinstitute.org

For a list of accredited courses, see
www.iwanttobealandscapearchitect.com

Lantra – the Sector Skills Council for the environmental and land-based sector. Tel: 0845 707 8007. www.lantra.co.uk and
www.afuturein.com

www.growcareers.info – a website, supported by various bodies including Lantra, that carries information on the range of careers relating to horticulture.

Materials scientist

Materials scientists study materials such as metals and alloys, glass, polymers and ceramics. They study the chemical and physical properties of these materials, how materials react to different conditions and stresses, how to prevent corrosion and fatigue, and disposal or re-use of materials after their productive life is over. Materials scientists often work at the cutting edge of new technology.

Materials scientists work in a range of different industries, including manufacturing, medical science, metal and mineral extraction, communications, as well as in research establishments. There are opportunities in research and development, manufacturing production and quality control.

Many people working in materials science are specialists in one particular material or process. Some of the specialist areas are described below.

- **Metallurgists** specialise in working with metals and alloys, such as iron, steel, tin and aluminium. Physical metallurgists focus on how metals perform under stress and at different temperatures, and so on; chemical metallurgists look at processes by which metals can be extracted from ores, and investigate issues like metal fatigue and corrosion, while process metallurgists focus on the ways metals can be handled in the production process.

- **Nanotechnologists** study and work with matter on an incredibly small scale – a nanometre is one-millionth of a millimetre. Being able to change and manipulate these tiny particles means that the properties of materials can be changed and adapted to a variety of new uses. As a result, nanotechnology is an area of huge investment. Examples of the application of nanotechnology include nanocoatings that prevent the spread of infections in hospitals by repelling dirt, and carbon nanotubes, which are 100 times stronger than steel but much lighter. Nanotechnology has potential in many areas, including healthcare, ICT, energy storage, manufacturing, environmental clean-up and space travel.

- **Polymer scientists/technologists** work on products made from polymers, which include plastics, rubber, adhesives and resins. Polymers are large molecules, with repeated structural units. They occur naturally, but can also be created. Synthetic polymers that have been created by polymer scientists include nylon, PVC, polystyrene and silicone. Polymer scientists are often involved in research and development, whereas polymer technologists work on the manufacturing processes involving polymers.

- **Textile technologists**, as the name suggests, work on textile materials such as yarns and fibres. They work in manufacturing, mainly in the production process. They have to understand the science of the fibres and their properties, such as robustness.

Entry qualifications

A degree is required. This could be in a subject such as materials science, materials science and engineering, metallurgy, materials engineering, polymer engineering, biomedical materials science, nanotechnology (perhaps combined with physics or chemistry) or aerospace materials. Alternatively, graduates with a general science or engineering degree may find opportunities, perhaps after gaining an appropriate postgraduate qualification.

Materials scientists need good problem solving skills, to be able to work accurately and pay attention to detail, good communication skills and the ability to work in a team with colleagues from different science and engineering disciplines.

Training and career development

Training is generally on the job and through short courses, perhaps through a graduate training scheme. It's possible to move into management, to work as a consultant on a self-employed basis or into teaching or lecturing on your subject in further or higher education. There are opportunities to work overseas.

Finding vacancies

Job vacancies are advertised on the website of the Institute of Materials, Minerals and Mining (see below) and the Institute of Nanotechnology also has a jobs page.

While at university, or as a recent graduate, you can access information about potential employers and current graduate vacancies through your university careers service. Further information about the help available through university careers services is provided in Chapter three.

Sources of further information

The Institute of Materials, Minerals & Mining (IOM3) – tel: 01476 513882. www.iom3.org

The Institute of Nanotechnology – tel: 01786 458020 www.nano.org.uk

Medical physicist

Medical physicists are clinical scientists who make use of their knowledge of physics to research and develop new techniques and equipment for the diagnosis and treatment of medical conditions. They are also involved in testing and monitoring existing techniques and maintaining high standards of quality and safety. The title of clinical scientist is protected by law, and refers to those scientists who have registered with the Health Professions Council (HPC).

There are opportunities for medical physicists to specialise in a number of different areas.

- **Radiotherapy,** for example, involves maintaining and calibrating the machines used to deliver radiation for the treatment of cancer.

- **Imaging physics** is concerned with monitoring the performance of X-ray machines, MRI (magnetic resonance imaging) scanners and so on.

- **Nuclear physics** is concerned with the administration of radioactive materials to patients and tracing their uptake using imaging scanners – in order to detect bone cancer, for example.

- **Renal dialysis** relates to the use of renal dialysis machines by patients suffering from kidney failure.

- **Radiation protection** is about ensuring that patients and staff are protected from accidental exposure to radiation – by enforcing health and safety procedures, disposing of radioactive waste and testing equipment.

- **Laser technology**, used for many different procedures from fragmenting kidney stones to cutting out cancerous tumours, involves maintaining and testing the equipment.

Most medical physicists work in NHS hospitals in departments of medical physics, clinical physics and bioengineering, medical electronics or medical biophysics. Some roles involve direct patient contact and close working with doctors and other healthcare workers.

Entry qualifications

Applicants for trainee medical physicist positions in the NHS usually need a first or upper second class degree in a physical science, engineering or related subject. Entry is also possible after gaining a masters degree in an appropriate subject.

Medical physicists also need good communication and teamworking skills, accuracy, attention to detail and an aptitude for problem solving.

Training and career development

Training usually involves following the Institute of Physics and Engineering in Medicine (IPEM) training programme, while working towards an IPEM-accredited masters degree. Candidates who successfully complete their training are awarded the Diploma of the IPEM, allowing them to register with the HPC.

With experience and appropriate skills, medical physicists can apply for promotion to senior roles in the NHS, following a structured career path. Such roles are likely to involve responsibility for managing and training other staff.

N.B. Training programmes and career structures for medical physicists are currently being revised, as part of the Modernising Scientific Careers programme. Changes will be implemented over the course of a few years, starting from 2010. For information, search for 'Modernising Scientific Careers' at: www.dh.gov.uk.

Finding vacancies

Hospitals advertise their vacancies for training positions in late November/December each year, with successful applicants commencing their employment in the following October. Undergraduates can apply during their final year of studies, provided they expect to achieve the first or upper second class degree required for entry.

Posts for trainees are advertised on the NHS Jobs website, in journals such as *New Scientist*, in the national press, on the IPEM's website and on the Recruitment Centre for Clinical Scientists website.

While at university, or as a recent graduate, you can access information about potential employers and current graduate vacancies through your university careers service. Further information about the help available through university careers services is provided in Chapter three.

Sources of further information

Health Professions Council (HPC) – tel: 020 7582 0866. www.hpc-uk.org

Institute of Physics and Engineering in Medicine (IPEM) – tel: 01904 610821. www.ipem.ac.uk

NHS Careers – tel: 0345 60 60 655. www.nhscareers.nhs.uk

NHS Wales Careers – tel: 01443 233472. www.nhswalescareers.com

Recruitment Centre for Clinical Scientists – for detailed information about training schemes and vacancies. Tel: 0871 433 3070. www.nhsclinicalscientists.info

www.jobs.nhs.uk – the job vacancy website for NHS employers across England and Wales.

Meteorologist

Meteorology is the study of our atmosphere, from the ground to the highest levels. Using highly sophisticated computer programs and mathematical models, meteorologists use data from various sources to make short- and long-term weather predictions. Apart from issuing weather forecasts for broadcast to the general public, meteorologists also provide specialist services to various industries and government bodies. The main areas of work are described below.

- **Operational meteorology** – the day-to-day collection and application of knowledge related to the weather, gathered from weather stations, satellites, observation vessels and aircraft. It includes the work of the TV, radio and press weather forecasters, staff who deal with enquiries and those who prepare forecasts for airlines and shipping.

- **Research** – meteorologists undertake research to improve the scope and accuracy of forecasting, and research the long-term effects of climate change.

- **Applied meteorology** – this covers the practical use of meteorological data in agriculture, forestry, fishing, civil aviation and many other industries. In this work, meteorologists may work in a team alongside other scientists and engineers.

The Met Office, a government agency, is the major UK employer of meteorologists and provides forecasting services as well as undertaking research. Many Met Office employees are based at its HQ in Exeter, but there are smaller offices throughout the UK and abroad. While the Met Office is mainly known for its public weather forecasts on radio, TV and the internet, it also provides services to local and national government departments and a wide range of industries including civil and military aviation, the oil and gas industries and the insurance industry.

Defence establishments, research institutes and university departments also employ meteorologists. Occasional openings to work abroad arise with the British Antarctic Survey and on aid programmes. Environmental consultancies and private weather forecasting services also employ meteorologists, and a few work for industrial firms such as the gas, oil, electricity and water industries.

Entry qualifications

Professional meteorologists usually have a degree in maths, physics or meteorology (often studied in combination with physics and maths). Other subjects, such as certain environmental science, physical chemistry, physical geography and computer science degrees, are acceptable.

For trainee forecasting posts with the Met Office, a good degree in maths, one of the physical sciences or meteorology is usually required. Applicants need physics to AS level, as a minimum. The Met Office also employs scientists for IT-based roles, such as the development of specialised scientific software, for which a physics or maths degree is normally required.

Postgraduate courses in meteorology are available. A good degree in maths or a physical science is the most usual entry route; certain environmental science, geography degrees etc may be acceptable for entry to some postgraduate courses.

Meteorologists need good communication skills and must be adaptable, analytical, methodical, observant and able to work accurately.

Training and career development

Trainees with the Met Office follow a Foundation Training Programme, delivered by the Met Office College and through on-the-job training.

With experience, meteorologists can apply for chartered status with the Royal Meteorological Society. Experienced meteorologists may also move into environmental consultancy services.

Finding vacancies

Vacancies with the Met Office are advertised on their website (see below). Vacancies for meteorologists may also be found in the national press and journals such as *New Scientist* and its associated website.

While at university, or as a recent graduate, you can access information about potential employers and current graduate vacancies through your university careers service. Further information about the help available through university careers services is provided in Chapter three.

Sources of further information

Met Office – tel: 0870 900 0100. www.metoffice.gov.uk

Royal Meteorological Society – tel: 0118 956 8500. Lists degree courses with a substantial meteorological content, and postgraduate courses. www.rmets.org/careers

Nuclear scientist

Nuclear scientists are interested in subatomic particles and their application in science. Areas of employment include the nuclear power industry, nuclear medicine and the field of nuclear weapons. Most nuclear scientists work with radioactive materials.

Nuclear power is produced by nuclear fission – the splitting of atoms into smaller parts. Nuclear scientists undertake research and development, and also work on the operation of power stations, to ensure that they operate as effectively, efficiently and, most importantly, as safely as possible. Nuclear decommissioning is another area of work.

In nuclear medicine, nuclear scientists work in research and development of medical techniques that make use of radioactive isotopes in medical diagnostic and screening services.

Depending on the role, the work may include both practical work, based in a laboratory or control room, and theoretical work – using sophisticated computer modelling programs.

EDF Energy is a major employer of nuclear scientists. The company operates eight nuclear power stations in the UK, and some new stations are being planned. Nuclear scientists are also employed by research institutes and in universities. For example, The Culham Centre for Fusion Energy, based in Oxfordshire, is the UK's national fusion research laboratory, researching the technique of nuclear fusion as a new source of clean energy. The Centre employs graduate physicists (and engineers).

Entry qualifications

For entry as a nuclear scientist with EDF Energy, you will need at least an upper second class honours degree in physics, chemistry, maths or materials science.

To undertake research, you will need a relevant degree and, often, postgraduate qualifications.

To work in nuclear science, you need good problem solving, analytical and communication skills. You need to be thorough and meticulous, and to be prepared to put safety as the top priority in your work.

Training and career development

EDF Energy operates a 12-month graduate training programme, during which graduates spend time at various locations, including two power stations, learning about the operations of the company. The programme includes about 18 weeks of formal training, in technical and business aspects of the work. Graduates are supported towards gaining professional membership of appropriate professional bodies.

The Culham Centre for Fusion Energy operates a two-year graduate development programme.

Finding vacancies

You can find out about opportunities at EDF Energy through the company's website www.edfenergy.com/careers. See www.culhamgraduatescheme. com for opportunities at the Culham Centre. Job vacancies in research may be advertised through journals such as *New Scientist* and its associated website. Physics-related vacancies are advertised on the website of the Institute of Physics (see below).

While at university, or as a recent graduate, you can access information about potential employers and current graduate vacancies through your university careers service. Further information about the help available through university careers services is provided in Chapter three.

Sources of further information

Institute of Physics – tel: 020 7470 4800. www.iop.org

Nuclear Industry Association – tel: 020 7766 6640. www.niauk.com

The Nuclear Institute – tel: 020 8695 8220. www.nuclearinst.com

Occupational hygienist

The role of the occupational hygienist is to reduce or prevent risks to health that may occur in the workplace. Health hazards that they are concerned with include chemicals, biological hazards (such as bacteria and viruses), physical conditions (such as heat, noise, vibration or radiation) and ergonomic hazards (such as machine design leading to poor posture).

Occupational hygienists use scientific, technological and management skills to understand how such hazards may affect the health of employees. Occupational hygienists assess how significant the effects are, and try to find practical, cost-effective ways of controlling the risks. They investigate risks related to both short- and long-term exposure to a hazard.

The work of occupational hygienists can involve hazard measurement and sampling, undertaking staff surveys, writing reports and giving recommendations. Occupational hygienists must keep themselves informed about scientific developments and legal requirements. In the course of their work, occupational hygienists liaise with a wide range of other professionals, including specialist doctors and nurses, safety officers and staff at all levels in the organisation – in particular senior managers.

Employers include occupational hygiene consultancies, which provide services on contract to employers, and large companies that employ in-house occupational hygienists, although in-house opportunities are declining. Some consultancies specialise in particular aspects of the work.

Entry qualifications

A degree is normally required. Most entrants have a degree in a scientific or technical subject, such as chemistry, physics, environmental science, engineering, environmental health or a medical science. Entrants to occupational hygiene often have relevant prior experience gained in industry. Sometimes, specialist knowledge in a particular field of science or engineering may be sought. It can be difficult for new graduates to enter, without industrial experience.

Relevant postgraduate qualifications may be an advantage for entry.

Occupational hygienists need good communication skills, an analytical mind and investigative and problem-solving skills. They also need persistence and the ability to work effectively with senior staff in organisations.

Training and career development

Training is mainly on the job. The British Occupational Hygiene Society offers a range of professional qualifications. Their Diploma of Professional Competence in Occupational Hygiene is available for those with a degree-level qualification in a scientific or related subject (although appropriate work experience can be acceptable in place of a degree) and at least five years' relevant experience. The Institute of Occupational Safety and Health also offers various professional development courses.

Finding vacancies

Jobs are advertised on www.healthandsafety-jobs.co.uk. Employers may also advertise vacancies on their own websites or through specialist recruitment agencies, and in the appointments sections of some national newspapers.

While at university, or as a recent graduate, you can access information about potential employers and current graduate vacancies through your university careers service. Further information about the help available through university careers services is provided in Chapter three.

Sources of further information

British Occupational Hygiene Society – tel: 01332 298101. www.bohs.org

Institution of Occupational Safety and Health (IOSH) – tel: 0116 257 3100. www.iosh.co.uk

Patent attorney

Most inventors use the skills of a patent attorney (sometimes known as a patent agent) to help them protect their work from being copied. By securing a patent for any new device or technical process they have developed, inventors can prevent their invention from being replicated for up to 20 years. To secure a patent, a detailed description of the invention has to be submitted for examination by an appropriate organisation. In the UK, the Intellectual Property Office (IPO) is the official body concerned with the protection of patents, designs, trademarks and copyright; there is also the European Patent Office (EPO).

The patent attorney advises the inventor on the likelihood of their invention being original, before drafting a patent and presenting it to the patent examiner. Most patent attorneys have a background in science or engineering in order to be able to best represent their clients.

Some large firms have their own patent departments dedicated to securing patents for their ongoing development projects. Alternatively, patent attorneys may work in private practice, possibly as partners in a firm of patent attorneys. Trainees tend to be taken on as **technical assistants**.

Entry qualifications

There are no specific qualifications required for work as a patent attorney. Degrees in a variety of scientific subjects may be accepted by employers; graduates may also come from technological, mathematical or engineering backgrounds.

Patent attorneys need the ability to communicate well with people and to write clearly and concisely. The work also demands analytical skills, accuracy and attention to detail. Foreign language skills may be beneficial, as the work increasingly has an international dimension.

Training and career development

Technical assistants train to become patent attorneys through self-study, external courses and some on-the-job training. To qualify for entry on the Register of Patent Agents can take four to six years of study and work experience. During this time, trainees need to undertake at least two years working under the close supervision of a qualified patent attorney and pass the examinations of the Chartered Institute of Patent Attorneys (CIPA).

To file patent applications before the EPO, patent attorneys must be on the list of European Patent Attorneys. This involves passing the European Qualifying Examination (EQE), which can be taken after three years' work experience and requires the ability to read French and German.

With experience, and appropriate business skills, qualified patent attorneys could think about going into private practice, either alone or in partnership with other patent attorneys.

Finding vacancies

Job vacancies are advertised by CIPA, on their website and in their supplement to *The CIPA Journal*. Jobs may also be advertised by specialist recruitment agencies and online job sites, in the appointment sections of certain daily newspapers and on employers' own websites.

While at university, or as a recent graduate, you can access information about potential employers and current graduate vacancies through your university careers service. Further information about the help available through university careers services is provided in Chapter three.

Sources of further information

The Chartered Institute of Patent Attorneys (CIPA) – tel: 020 7405 9450. www.cipa.org.uk

The Intellectual Property Office – tel: 0845 9500 505. www.ipo.gov.uk

Intellectual Property Regulation Board (IPReg) – tel: 020 7353 4373. www.ipreg.org.uk

Patent examiner

Around 300 patent examiners work for the Intellectual Property Office (IPO), the official UK body concerned with the protection of patents, designs, trademarks and copyright. In order to grant a patent (the legal right to prevent a new invention from being copied), the examiner must have the appropriate skills and knowledge to understand the applications made to them, most of which relate to scientific or technological devices or processes.

On receipt of an application for a patent, all documents submitted have to be carefully dated, checked and studied. The examiner then starts a preliminary search of existing UK and international patent specifications, technical publications and online information, making certain that the claimed invention is not simply a development of an existing product. Details of the application are published once the search is complete, to allow anyone to study it. Following this, an in-depth examination is carried out that includes investigating in detail the novelty and inventiveness of the invention. This process may involve discussions and correspondence with the patent attorney. It can take years before all the legal and technical requirements are met and a patent is granted. If the application fails, the examiner compiles a detailed report explaining the legal reasons for why the patent was refused.

Entry qualifications

A degree in a scientific subject is acceptable for entry into this type of work (degrees in maths and engineering, or equivalent qualifications/ experience are also accepted).

Patent examiners need analytical skills and the ability to clearly explain complex concepts (both technical and legal).

Training and career development

Patent examiners receive in-house training in the principles of intellectual property law. They also work on real patent applications, while under the supervision of senior examiners. If necessary, it is possible to study a foreign language as part of the training. Examiners are encouraged to work towards a postgraduate qualification part time while they are working.

There is a structured career path within the IPO, with opportunities for promotion as and when you reach an appropriate level of performance during the first few years in the role. More senior roles, such as at deputy director level and above, are awarded through competition.

Finding vacancies

Jobs are advertised on the IPO's website and in the national and local press. While at university, or as a recent graduate, you can access information about potential employers and current graduate vacancies through your university careers service. Further information about the help available through university careers services is provided in Chapter three.

Sources of further information

The Intellectual Property Office – tel: 0845 9500 505.
www.ipo.gov.uk

Pharmacologist

Pharmacology is the study of the effects of drugs and chemicals on living things. Pharmacologists are therefore involved in researching and developing new and existing drugs, such as pain killers, antibiotics, antihistamines and so on. The work can involve, for example, investigating how effective and safe a drug is; researching ways of improving a drug, or the way it is administered; or developing an entirely new drug.

Drug research and development is a hugely expensive process, in both time and money. It can cost up to £500 million and take up to 12 years to take a drug from patent stage to a commercial launch. During that time, the potential drug will have been rigorously tested by pharmacologists. Early experiments are carried out on small mammals, or on cultured cells or tissue samples. Pharmacologists design and carry out tests to discover how the drug is absorbed and then cleared by the body. In the latter stages of development, the drug will be tested on healthy human volunteers, and finally on patients.

There are opportunities for pharmacologists to work in pharmaceutical companies, in universities (undertaking research and teaching a wide range of students, including doctors, dentists, nurses, vets, pharmacists and so on), in research institutions, government departments and in hospitals, performing clinical trials.

Entry qualifications

Entry is possible with a degree or postgraduate qualification in pharmacology. Acceptable degree subjects for entry onto postgraduate courses include physiology, biochemistry, pharmacy and medicine.

Pharmacologists need plenty of patience and perseverance. They must work very accurately, paying great attention to the finest detail. Excellent observation skills are a must.

Training and career development

Training is usually on the job and may involve learning about specialist equipment and research techniques. You may also need to attend short courses or conferences in order to keep up to date with developments in this field. Once in employment, it may be possible to study for a postgraduate qualification on a part-time basis. A higher degree, such as a PhD or MSc, may be beneficial for career progression.

Pharmacologists may be promoted to team leaders and then into senior management roles. It may also be possible to branch out into sales, marketing or public relations for a pharmaceutical company, into medical information and publishing, into toxicology work, or into environmental research on pollutants.

Finding vacancies

Jobs are advertised on the British Pharmacological Society website and in journals such as *New Scientist* and its associated website. Jobs may also be advertised by specialist recruitment agencies and online job sites, in the appointment sections of certain daily newspapers and on employers' own websites.

While at university, or as a recent graduate, you can access information about potential employers and current graduate vacancies through your university careers service. Further information about the help available through university careers services is provided in Chapter three.

Sources of further information

Association of the British Pharmaceutical Industry – tel: 0870 890 4333. www.abpi-careers.org.uk

British Pharmacological Society (BPS) – tel: 020 7239 0171. www.bps.ac.uk and www.careersinpharmacology.org

Public analyst

Public analysts are concerned with investigating all sorts of incidents and problems that may have had a detrimental affect on public health and safety. There are around 25 laboratories in the UK that make up the Public Analysts' Laboratory Service. Cases are brought to the attention of the public analysts at these facilities by trading standards and environmental health departments. These may relate to chemical spillages, animal diseases or other problems in the food chain, contaminated water supplies and so on.

There are approximately 70 public analysts in the UK, who are highly qualified and experienced chemists. They are assisted by laboratory staff, usually qualified at least to degree level. Together they test, analyse and inspect a variety of products and samples, such as food, household goods, medicines, cosmetics, river water, toxic waste, animal feed and fertilisers – in fact, any item that may have broken the law in relation to public health and safety. Most laboratories also provide a commercial service to local industry, when highly sophisticated laboratory services are required.

Public analysts also have a wider scientific role that involves providing information and advice, such as in relation to new legislation, food labelling, interpreting EU regulations and so on. They act as expert witnesses in court proceedings, if cases result in legal action.

Entry qualifications

Professional training begins with a degree in chemistry, preferably including analytical chemistry. Laboratory staff who assist public analysts may come from a range of scientific backgrounds, holding degrees in subjects such as chemistry, food science and microbiology.

The work requires a methodical and painstaking approach, with great attention to detail. Numeracy and ICT skills are also important. Public analysts need excellent communication skills and an interest in scientific developments.

Training and career development

By law, a public analyst must hold the Mastership in Chemical Analysis (MChemA) awarded by the Royal Society of Chemistry (RSC). This requires membership of the RSC plus several years of study and work experience.

Training for laboratory staff is likely to be on the job, and involves short courses to learn about particular analytical techniques and equipment, as well as attendance at conferences and exhibitions to keep up to date with developments in the field. Graduate employees may be able to study part time for postgraduate qualifications such as an MSc in analytical chemistry, which offers partial exemption from the MChemA examinations.

Finding vacancies

Contact details of all of the public analyst laboratories in the UK can be found on the website of the Association of Public Analysts (APA). These laboratories advertise their junior positions locally and also through the APA website. Posts for qualified public analysts are advertised in journals such as *Chemistry World* and *New Scientist.*

While at university, or as a recent graduate, you can access information about potential employers and current graduate vacancies through your university careers service. Further information about the help available through university careers services is provided in Chapter three.

Sources of further information

The Association of Public Analysts – www.publicanalyst.com

Royal Society of Chemistry (RSC) – tel: 020 7437 8656. www.rsc.org/mchema

Research scientist

Scientists involved in **applied research** have the aim of developing new or improved techniques or products, which will typically solve a particular problem or have some commercial application. This contrasts with **pure research** (sometimes known as basic or fundamental research), which aims to increase our understanding of the world around us by making fundamental discoveries, but which may not have an immediate practical use (if at all).

Throughout this chapter, there are examples of jobs where it is possible to work in research – from acoustician to zoologist! In addition, there are opportunities for research scientists in a wide range of other scientific branches. Just a few examples are shown below.

- **Bacteriology** – research in this area may focus on identifying new species of bacteria; alternatively, it may involve finding new ways of diagnosing and treating the diseases caused by bacteria in animals, humans and plants.

- **Ecology** – concerned with all types of organisms (i.e. living things, including plants, animals, fungus and bacteria) and their relationships to one another (i.e. ecosystems). Research in this area offers many different opportunities from studying butterfly migration patterns to investigating how plants compete against each other for light and nutrients.

- **Entomology** – the study of insects. Research may relate to insect pest control, the problem of declining bee populations or field studies of species of evolutionary significance, for example.

- **Electrochemistry** – is concerned with how electricity can produce chemical reactions, and vice versa. Research may have the aim of finding new industrial metal finishing processes or developing new types of batteries, for example.

- **Freshwater biology** – researchers may study patterns of species that inhabit lakes, or the effects of flooding and drought on plant and fish species in rivers, for instance.

- **Genetics** – the science of genetics and inherited traits. Researchers may, for example, seek to identify the different genes that cause birth defects or particular diseases, how plants can be genetically modified to grow stronger and larger, or ways of improving DNA-profiling to help solve crimes.

- **Medical research** – there are numerous branches of research that seek either to improve our health, or improve the diagnosis, treatment and prevention of diseases. Research may range from population studies, such as looking at how our lifestyles affect our wellbeing, to research at the molecular level, into infections, toxins and drugs.

- **Organic chemistry** – relates to those compounds that contain carbon, such as enzymes, proteins, plastics and so on. There are many research opportunities in organic chemistry, from determining the structure of newly discovered molecules to creating synthetic compounds.

- **Particle physics** – researchers investigate theories about the smallest particles of matter, and the forces that act between them, and therefore seek to answer the most fundamental questions about how the universe came into being.

- **Solid-state physics** – is concerned with the physical structure and properties of solids, such as their thermodynamic and electromagnetic qualities. Research may focus on developing new materials and alloys, or investigating applications for nanotechnology or semiconductors, for example.

The exact nature of scientific research varies according to the particular field of science involved. For example, scientists working in the biological sciences may have the opportunity to make field trips around the world, to study natural habitats and environments. Other research may be laboratory-based, at a workbench perhaps using highly complex equipment. In practice, research usually means repeatedly performing experiments or making observations, and collecting, recording, managing and analysing the results. Computers are frequently used to aid the design of experiments, analyse the data obtained from them and make predictions based on the results.

A great deal of research is undertaken on a project basis, meaning that researchers are often employed on short-term contracts. The research team, lead by a senior researcher, may be responsible for defining the aims and methodology of the research project, preparing an application for a grant to fund the research, making presentations on the progress and outcome of their work and publishing their findings in scientific journals for review by other scientists.

In industry, scientists may work as part of research and development (R&D) teams, with the combined role of researching new ideas and developing them into viable, commercial products. Researchers may therefore be permanent employees of commercial firms or consultancies.

The publicly funded Research Councils invest around £3 billion each year in various research projects, supporting over 30,000 researchers at any one time, including doctoral students, research staff in universities and research institutes, and research fellows. Research opportunities also exist in industry, with consultancies and with charities, such as the British Heart Foundation and Cancer Research UK.

Entry qualifications

Most research scientists in academic settings have achieved a postgraduate qualification, usually a PhD (a doctoral degree). Graduates usually need an upper second or first class degree in a relevant subject in order to begin a PhD.

In industry, entry may be possible for graduates as research assistants or at technician level. It may be possible to study for higher degrees part time while in employment and this may be required for career progression.

To work as a research scientist you need a passion for the subject you are researching. You also need to be dedicated and determined; from finding funding to undertaking painstaking experiments that may not lead to any new discoveries, researchers need to be able to get past many hurdles. Teamworking and communication skills are also important, as is integrity and a methodical approach to your work.

Training and career development

Training may include attending courses, seminars and conferences, possibly overseas, to keep up to date with developments in the field, or to present your own research. Researchers also need to read scientific journals and network with other scientists to keep pace with related work being undertaken in their field of interest.

With appropriate qualifications, it may be possible to become a member of a relevant society or institution, such as the Institute of Physics, Royal Society of Chemistry or Society of Biology. Such institutions offer events and courses in support of your continuing professional development (CPD).

Postdoctoral researchers may find fixed-term positions assisting in academic research. In some cases, having gained experience on several different projects, this may lead to a permanent position in the university department as a university researcher or lecturer. There are some funded postdoctoral fellowships, which allow researchers to run their own projects.

Finding vacancies

The Research Councils advertise details of their studentships (funded PhD places) and fellowships (funded positions for senior academic researchers) on their websites. Universities also advertise their research opportunities on their own websites or on the graduate careers website www.prospects.ac.uk. Positions may also be advertised in scientific journals such as *New Scientist* and its associated website, by specialist recruitment agencies and online job sites, and on employers' own websites.

While at university, or as a recent graduate, you can access information about potential employers and current graduate vacancies through your university careers service. Further information about the help available through university careers services is provided in Chapter three.

Sources of further information

Biotechnology and Biological Sciences Research Council (BBSRC)
– tel: 01793 413200. www.bbsrc.ac.uk

Engineering and Physical Sciences Research Council (EPSRC) –
tel: 01793 444100. www.epsrc.ac.uk

Institute of Physics (IOP) - tel: 020 7470 4800. www.iop.org

Medical Research Council (MRC) - tel: 020 7636 5422. www.mrc.ac.uk

Natural Environment Research Council (NERC) - tel: 01793 411500. www.nerc.ac.uk

Research Councils UK - www.rcuk.ac.uk

Royal Society of Chemistry (RSC) - tel: 020 7437 8656. www.rsc.org

Science & Technology Facilities Council (STFC) - tel: 01793 442000. www.stfc.ac.uk

Society of Biology - tel: 020 7936 5900. www.societyofbiology.org

http://ec.europa.eu/euraxess - the EURAXESS *Researchers in Motion* website is a joint initiative between the European Commission and those countries participating in the European Union's Framework Programme for Research. It carries adverts for research posts across the EU, as well as information for researchers looking to work in Europe.

Sport and exercise scientist

Sport and exercise scientists use their knowledge of physiology, psychology and biomechanics to help elite athletes, as well as members of the general public, improve their performance in sport and exercise. Competition for posts can be intense as there is a growing interest in this type of work.

In general, sport and exercise scientists take an interdisciplinary approach, although it is also possible to specialise in any of the three component sciences:

- biomechanics - concerns human movement and the body's interaction with equipment and apparatus

- physiology - relates to how the body responds to physical exertion

- psychology - is about understanding and managing the emotional and behavioural aspects of sporting performance.

Some sport and exercise scientists specialise in particular sports, such as football, athletics, rugby etc or in various types of exercise - from clinical applications of exercise to recreational exercise in gyms, sports centres and so on.

At elite level, sport and exercise scientists may work with individual top athletes or whole teams, testing their fitness, monitoring and evaluating their technique, developing training programmes and so on. There are opportunities with the home country Institutes of Sport, the national governing bodies and with some professional sports teams and individuals.

Sport and exercise scientists can also work with the general public in a variety of settings such as local authority leisure centres and private gyms. This may be combined with the role of personal trainer or fitness instructor, which requires separate training.

Alternatively, there are opportunities for sport and exercise scientists to work with patients undergoing rehabilitation within the NHS or with private healthcare providers. There are also opportunities in university departments, health promotion, and sport and exercise development work, which may not involve direct involvement with athletes.

Entry qualifications

It is possible to work as a sport and exercise scientist with either a degree or postgraduate qualification in sport and exercise science. Entry onto a postgraduate course may be possible for graduates with degrees in relevant subjects, such as physiology. However, postgraduate qualifications usually aim to develop you as a specialist in a particular aspect of sport and exercise science and therefore most require your first degree to be in sport and exercise science as a basis for further learning. The British Association of Sport and Exercise Sciences (BASES) endorses some undergraduate and postgraduate courses; visit the association's website for full details.

Sport and exercise scientists need good communication skills and the ability to encourage and motivate people. They also need to be able to analyse data and solve problems creatively.

Training and career development

It is possible to become a BASES accredited sport and exercise scientist by undertaking the BASES Supervised Experience scheme. This takes a minimum of two years and involves gaining a postgraduate degree, attending workshops and completing at least 500 hours of supervised practice. While undertaking supervised experience, applicants can use the title 'probationary sport and exercise scientist'.

Once qualified, sports and exercise scientists are expected to remain up to date with developments in the subject through workshops, conferences and by reading academic journals.

There is no formal career structure for sport and exercise scientists and your prospects for promotion will vary according to your particular area of work. There may be opportunities to become self-employed, and to work or travel abroad.

Finding vacancies

Vacancies are advertised on BASES' website and by some of the institutions and associations listed below. Jobs may also be advertised by specialist recruitment agencies and online job sites, and on employers' own websites.

While at university, or as a recent graduate, you can access information about potential employers and current graduate vacancies through your university careers service. Further information about the help available through university careers services is provided in Chapter three.

Sources of further information

The British Association of Sport and Exercise Sciences (BASES) – tel: 0113 812 6162. www.bases.org.uk

British Olympic Association – tel: 0207 842 5700. www.olympics.org.uk

British Paralympic Association – tel: 020 7842 5789. www.paralympics.org.uk

English Institute of Sport – tel: 0870 759 0400. www.eis2win.co.uk

SkillsActive – the Sector Skills Council for the active leisure and learning sector. Tel: 08000 933300 (careers advice line). www.skillsactive.com/careers

Sports Institute Northern Ireland – tel: 028 9036 8295. www.sini.co.uk

SportScotland Institute of Sport – tel: 01786 460100. www.sisport.com

UK Sport – tel: 020 7211 5100. www.uksport.gov.uk

Welsh Institute of Sport – tel: 0845 045 0902. www.welsh-institute-sport.co.uk

Surveyor

Surveying is a term that covers many different jobs. What they have in common is that they can all involve the measurement, valuation, management and development of physical assets and resources. Built environment and property surveying may be the most widely known areas of work, and include quantity surveying (managing the financial aspects of construction projects), building surveying (advising on the physical condition of properties and supervising their development) and valuation (estimating the value of property, land and business assets). However, there are several other branches of surveying, for which a scientific background is particularly beneficial.

Environment surveying is concerned with the environmental aspects of land, property and construction. Work in this area may involve:

- advising on ways of treating contaminated land
- managing the preparation of environmental assessments
- carrying out environmental audits
- advising on the impact of construction projects on the environment (ecology, soil, water and air)
- collecting samples for testing and interpreting laboratory results
- advising on the management of specific habitats and species.

Geomatic surveying covers a wide range of work to do with surveying the land and sea. This may include:

- undertaking environmental assessments
- advising on the impact of alternative energies and sustainability
- analysing data from geographical information systems (GIS)
- applying a knowledge of rock and soil mechanics to problems relating to slope and ground instability
- measuring the physical features of marine environments (inland waters, rivers, ports, oceans etc)
- advising on the management of landscapes and natural habitats

- surveying the marine environment to gauge the value of physical, biological and chemical resources within the sea.

Minerals and waste surveying involves applying surveying skills to the mining, minerals and waste management industries. Surveyors in this line of work may:

- interpret laboratory analyses of contaminated land and advise on remedial treatments

- make recommendations based on environmental assessments

- analyse the results of rock and soil tests

- assess the economic and technical viability of sites for mineral extraction

- monitor the environmental impact of waste management facilities.

Planning and development surveying is concerned primarily with the physical aspects of the built environment, but it also touches on the environmental and social aspects, such as advising on environmental laws and sustainable designs.

Rural surveying relates to consultancy, valuation and management of all aspects of the rural economy, including agriculture, forestry and coastal land. Surveyors working in this area may be involved in:

- advising on agricultural methods and livestock management

- preparing woodland management plans

- applying an understanding of nature conservation to development projects

- dealing with sustainability issues.

Surveyors may work for a variety of different employers including surveying consultancies, construction companies and building contractors, research organisations and public sector bodies, such as local authorities and hospitals. The work, although office based, involves being out and about much of the time.

Entry qualifications

The Royal Institution of Chartered Surveyors (RICS) is the main professional body for this type of work, although there are others. To become a chartered surveyor with RICS, you need a RICS-accredited degree or postgraduate qualification. Graduates with a degree from a range of scientific subjects may be accepted for entry onto an accredited postgraduate course. Other professional bodies have their own entry requirements; which organisation you choose may depend on your particular specialism.

Surveyors need an analytical and logical approach to their work. Good communication skills are essential, and it is important that you are able to work well in a team. The work often calls for organisational and practical problem-solving skills, and the ability to work under pressure and manage projects.

Training and career development

To achieve chartered status with RICS, you must complete a period of structured training with an employer before undertaking the Assessment of Professional Competence (APC).

With experience it may be possible to move into senior roles, or to specialise in aspects such as contract or project management. Many surveyors become self-employed and it is also possible to go into private practice with other surveyors. There are good opportunities for working overseas.

Finding vacancies

Vacancies are advertised by RICS and other professional bodies via their websites and associated journals. Jobs may also be advertised by specialist recruitment agencies and online job sites, in the recruitment sections of certain newspapers and on employers' own websites.

While at university, or as a recent graduate, you can access information about potential employers and current graduate vacancies through your university careers service. Further information about the help available through university careers services is provided in Chapter three.

Sources of further information

Royal Institution of Chartered Surveyors (RICS) – tel: 0870 333 1600. www.rics.org/careers

Technical brewer

From the few simple ingredients of malted barley, hops, yeast and water, beer is produced by a complicated, biochemical process. In order to mass-produce beer to the same standard, flavour and strength time after time takes technical skill and scientific knowledge. Some brewers still make beer by traditional methods, while others use modern techniques to produce keg beers and lagers.

Technical brewers supervise the brewing process and oversee all the recipes and ingredients. They need a good understanding of the engineering and biochemical processes involved. In a large brewery, each brewer is likely to specialise in a particular area, such as fermentation, filtration or packaging. In a small firm, a single brewer may be responsible for all stages of production.

Despite the fact that, every day, people in Britain consume around 25 million pints of beer, ale, lager and stout, technical brewers make up a very small profession. There are only around 400 technical brewers in the UK, most of whom work for the large, multinational breweries. There may also be some opportunities with independent local firms, and smaller, so-called, microbreweries.

Breweries also offer opportunities for laboratory-based scientists working in research and development and quality control. The work may involve analysing raw ingredients and finished products to ensure their quality, or advising on how to adapt technical processes in order to produce consistent results from variable raw ingredients, for example.

In recent years, there has been a revival in the popularity of cider, and cider makers, mostly based in the south and west of England, recruit scientists for roles similar to those found in brewing.

Entry qualifications

Technical brewers are usually graduates with degrees in subjects such as microbiology, chemistry, food science or chemical engineering. Heriot-Watt University in Edinburgh offers relevant postgraduate courses, available via distance learning. Other laboratory-based scientists may have degrees in botany, chemistry, microbiology or biochemistry, for example.

The work requires accuracy and a logical approach. Technical brewers need to be able to communicate effectively and lead a team of production workers. It is also important to have an understanding of hygiene issues and the general commercial aspects of business.

Training and career development

Training is on the job and may involve studying for the professional exams of the Institute of Brewing and Distilling (IBD), ultimately leading to Master Brewer status. It may be possible to gain postgraduate qualifications part time, while in employment. It is likely that employers would expect you to undergo continuing professional development (CPD) throughout your career, by attending industry events and relevant short courses.

With experience, it may be possible for technical brewers to gain promotion to technical director or senior brewer. Scientists involved in laboratory work may become team leaders or move into general management. For those with the necessary business skills, as well as technical expertise, it may be possible to open and run their own microbrewery.

Finding vacancies

Vacancies may be advertised in journals such as *New Scientist* and the IBD's *Brewer & Distiller International*. Jobs are also advertised by the journal *Brewers' Guardian*, which is only available to people working in the industry, although an online version can be viewed at www.brewersguardian.com. Jobs may also be advertised by specialist recruitment agencies and online job sites, in the recruitment sections of certain newspapers and on employers' own websites.

While at university, or as a recent graduate, you can access information about potential employers and current graduate vacancies through your university careers service. Further information about the help available through university careers services is provided in Chapter three.

Sources of further information

British Beer & Pub Association – tel: 020 7627 9191. www.beerandpub.com

Heriot-Watt University – International Centre for Brewing & Distilling – tel: 0131 451 3183. www.icbd.hw.ac.uk

Institute of Brewing & Distilling – tel: 020 7499 8144. www.ibd.org.uk

Society of Independent Brewers – tel: 0845 337 9158. http://siba.co.uk

Toxicologist

Toxicology is the study of the harmful effects of chemicals on living organisms – humans, animals and plants etc. We come into contact with chemicals in many different aspects of our lives, such as the drugs we use to treat illnesses, the cleaning products, paints and so on we use at home, the chemicals used to clean and treat our drinking water and the pesticides used to protect crops. In normal situations, these bring great benefits to us, but problems can arise through overdoses, accidental spillages and improper use of chemicals. Toxicologists are the experts in detecting and treating the effects of poisoning, and in advising on ways to protect people and the environment from pollutants.

Toxicologists can work in a number of different areas, depending on their interests. The main opportunities are as follows.

- **Industrial toxicologists** test raw materials and finished products for their toxic potential or for contamination. Companies involved in manufacturing products such as pharmaceuticals, petrochemicals, agrochemicals, household goods, food and drink, and cosmetics, all rely on toxicologists. Some may be employed directly by the manufacturer; others may work on contract through independent laboratories.

- **Pharmaceutical toxicologists** work in drug development, testing the safety of new products in terms of whether they cause skin or eye irritation, how the body's organs react to the drug, and whether long-term use of the drug can cause cancer, for example. Toxicologists need to use a variety of experimental techniques, including animal testing, to fully understand the toxic potential of each new drug in development.

- **Academic toxicologists** undertake research in collaboration with industry, Research Councils, charities and so on, while also teaching students in higher education. Some academics also work on Government advisory committees as independent experts.

- **Clinical toxicologists** are medically-qualified specialists who work in hospitals treating patients who have been poisoned and providing support to other clinical staff through the National Poisons Information Service.

- **Forensic toxicologists** investigate and act as expert witnesses in legal cases in which drugs or chemicals have been a factor. They may test for the presence, and effects, of chemicals in cases relating to suicide or murder, drink driving, accidental overdoses and so on.

- **Ecotoxicologists** are concerned with the effects of chemicals in the environment and on ecosystems. They may track pollutants through the food chain or look for changes in the biology of various organisms, such as their ability to reproduce. Researchers may work for environmental agencies or charities, combining work in the field with laboratory experimentation.

- **Regulatory toxicologists** work for the Government in setting standards and advising on issues to do with toxicology.

- **Occupational toxicologists** work in areas similar to industrial toxicologists, but are involved in advising on how people can work safely with potentially harmful raw materials, finished products and waste materials, or in dealing with accidental exposure to toxic chemicals.

Entry qualifications

At degree level, toxicology may be taught as part of, or in combination with, other scientific subjects such as pharmacology or biochemistry. Graduates in subjects such as biology, chemistry, biochemistry, pharmacology, immunology, medicine, physiology or environmental science may also gain entry to this type of work after taking postgraduate qualifications specialising in toxicology.

The work requires good attention to detail and the ability to interpret and assess large amounts of data. Practical laboratory skills are required, as are report writing and communication skills.

Training and career development

Training is likely to be on the job and involve attending short courses, workshops, conferences and seminars in order to learn specific techniques and to keep up to date with developments in the field. A higher degree, such as a PhD, may be beneficial for career progression. It may be possible to work towards a professional diploma, such as:

- the Diploma of the Royal College of Pathology – part 1 of membership

- the International Diploma in Toxicology, offered by the Society of Biology

- the Diploma of the American Board of Toxicology.

With appropriate qualifications and experience it is possible to join the UK Register of Toxicologists, administered by the Society of Biology and the British Toxicology Society. Registered toxicologists are expected to undertake continuing professional development (CPD) throughout their careers.

Finding vacancies

The British Toxicology Society advertises vacancies on its website; jobs are also advertised in *New Scientist* and its associated website. Jobs may be advertised by specialist recruitment agencies and online job sites, in the recruitment sections of certain newspapers and on employers' own websites.

While at university, or as a recent graduate, you can access information about potential employers and current graduate vacancies through your university careers service. Further information about the help available through university careers services is provided in Chapter three.

Sources of further information

American Board of Toxicology – www.abtox.org

Association of the British Pharmaceutical Industry (ABPI) – tel: 0870 890 4333. www.abpi.org.uk and www.abpicareers.org.uk

The British Toxicology Society – tel: 01206 226059. www.thebts.org

The Royal College of Pathology – tel: 020 7451 6700. www.rcpath.org

Society of Biology – tel: 020 7936 5900. www.societyofbiology.org

The UK Register of Toxicologists – www.toxreg.org.uk

Waste/Recycling manager

We live in a world that produces huge quantities of waste – domestic, commercial and industrial. Over 330 million tonnes of waste are produced each year in the UK alone. Controlling and disposing of that waste is a very technical and complex process, combining aspects of chemistry, geology, civil engineering and economics. There are also legal considerations, with strict laws on pollution and the methods used to dispose of certain wastes. Managers are needed in both the public and the private sectors in order to oversee waste storage, transport and disposal, as well as to plan and regulate activities.

On a day-to-day basis, managers may be required to supervise teams of operatives and contractors and ensure operations run efficiently, within budget and in compliance with regulations. They may be involved in planning and developing new schemes for waste management, such as a new kerbside collection for household food waste. The work also involves report writing and data collection, as well as public relations work, such as consulting on and promoting new schemes and responding to media enquiries.

Managers may specialise in waste collection and disposal operations. Local authorities are responsible for household waste and recycling (as well as for some commercial waste and recycling), but out-sourced contractors often provide the service. Many large, industrial companies manage the disposal of their own waste and materials for recycling. Certain industrial, hazardous and chemical wastes have to be dealt with in specific ways – burned in high-temperature incinerators, or treated by special processes. Providing sustainable and cleaner waste treatment processes is becoming increasingly important, as burying waste to decompose in landfill sites is used only as a last resort.

In addition to waste disposal, there are also opportunities for managers to work in waste recycling. Local authorities are responsible for providing kerbside collections and recycling centres where the public can bring paper, glass, aluminium and a wide range of other materials. Some local authorities have set up 'energy from waste' plants where, for example, waste can be burned to produce heat for domestic heating and electricity.

Finally, there are career opportunities in regulation, inspecting and monitoring waste management facilities, and checking that the law is being upheld. In England and Wales, the Environment Agency oversees the transportation, treatment and disposal of waste.

Entry qualifications

Waste/recycling management officers come from a variety of backgrounds, and degrees in subjects such as environmental science, geology, biology, chemistry may all prove useful. A number of relevant postgraduate qualifications are available for those with a suitable first degree.

To work in waste/recycling management, you need practical problem-solving skills and the ability to work as part of a team. You also need to be able to understand and use complex reports and studies, and communicate effectively with non-technical colleagues.

Training and career development

Training is likely to be on the job and involve attending short courses and conferences. It may be possible to study for a postgraduate qualification on a part-time basis while in employment. By law, certain types of waste management facilities require an environmental permit to operate in England and Wales. A condition of the permit is that operators (either individuals or organisations) must demonstrate continuing technical competence through an approved waste operator competence scheme. An individual's technical competence may be demonstrated through appropriate training, qualifications and experience.

Due to a greater environmental awareness among the general public, together with Government commitment to reducing waste, there are increasing opportunities for work at a senior level. Waste management officers can also specialise as consultants, advising on matters such as environmental impacts, risk assessment and quality assurance.

Finding vacancies

Local authority vacancies are advertised on www.LGjobs.com. Jobs are also advertised by the Chartered Institution of Wastes Management (CIWM), in its members' journal and on its website. Employers may also advertise vacancies on their own websites, in the appointments sections of certain daily newspapers or through specialist recruitment agencies and online job sites.

While at university, or as a recent graduate, you can access information about potential employers and current graduate vacancies through your university careers service. Further information about the help available through university careers services is provided in Chapter three.

Sources of further information

The Chartered Institution of Wastes Management (CIWM) – tel: 01604 620426. www.ciwm.co.uk

Energy & Utility Skills – the Sector Skills Council covering waste management. Tel: 0845 077 9922. www.euskills.co.uk/careers

Environment Agency – tel: 08708 506506. www.environment-agency.gov.uk

Environmental Services Association – tel: 020 7824 8882. www.esauk.org

Waste Management Industry Training and Advisory Board (WAMITAB) – tel: 01604 231950. www.wamitab.org.uk

Zoologist

A zoologist, or animal scientist, specialises in the study of animals. The term 'animal' covers living organisms from mammals, fish and birds through to insects and single celled organisms.

Many zoologists undertake research, studying, for example, animal evolution, animal behaviour, physiology (how cells, tissues and organs function), genetics or species' interaction with their environment. Research may be undertaken to conserve endangered species, prevent disease or find improved methods of pest control, for example, or may be 'pure' research, to find out more about a particular species – information which could eventually have a practical application.

Zoologists generally specialise in a particular group or species of animals. They may undertake research in the field (studying the animal in its natural habitat), or focus on animals in captivity, or the work could be primarily laboratory based. The data collected must be analysed and interpreted and the job generally involves contributing to writing scientific papers and, possibly, presenting findings at conferences.

Zoologists may be employed by research institutes and universities, large zoos and wildlife parks, conservation organisations and charities and government agencies. Other openings are found in pharmaceutical companies, large museums and with some government bodies where zoologists help to develop policies relating to animal health and welfare.

If working in higher education, lecturing may also form part of the work. Zoologists employed in zoos would generally have overall responsibility for a particular group of animals in the zoo, while zoologists working for conservation organisations may be involved in programmes to increase the numbers of a particular species, or in programmes to release animals back into their natural habitat.

Entry qualifications

You need a degree in zoology/animal biology or animal science and, possibly, a specialist postgraduate qualification.

Zoologists need good observation, problem solving and written and verbal communication skills, the ability to work well with a team, and to be methodical and patient.

Training and career development

If working in higher education, you may be expected to gain a PhD (research degree). Many zoologists become members of the professional bodies listed below.

Finding vacancies

Entry is competitive, so finding a job that is based primarily on zoology is not easy. You may need to take a postgraduate qualification to specialise in a particular area. Any relevant work experience will be an advantage. Research jobs are usually offered on a fixed-term basis, for the duration of the funding period of a project. Vacancies may be advertised in journals such as *Nature* or *New Scientist* and their associated websites.

While at university, or as a recent graduate, you can access information about potential employers and current graduate vacancies through your university careers service. Further information about the help available through university careers services is provided in Chapter three.

Sources of further information

Institute of Biology – tel: 020 7936 5900. www.iob.org

Institute of Zoology – tel: 020 7449 6610. www.zsl.org/science

Zoological Society of London – tel: 020 7722 3333. www.zsl.org

Chapter seven

Health-related careers

"Say aaargh!"

BILL

By their very nature, many health-related careers require you to have an interest in, and understanding of, science. This chapter describes some of the roles that require a specific degree in a vocational subject either for direct entry into employment or to progress onto further training. So if you are still at school or college, and are interested in science, you might want to consider undertaking a health-related vocational course leading to one of the careers described here.

The career areas included in this chapter are:

- biomedical scientist
- clinical physiologist
- dentist
- dietitian

- doctor
- midwife
- nurse
- nutritionist
- optometrist
- orthoptist
- pharmacist
- physiotherapist
- radiographer
- veterinary surgeon.

There are also other health-related careers that do not require a specific vocational degree and are, therefore, an option for graduates with degrees from a range of scientific subjects. The roles of clinical perfusion scientist, clinical scientist and medical physicist are examples, and are described in Chapter six.

Regarding funding arrangements for training, note that students offered NHS-funded places on either undergraduate or postgraduate programmes leading to registration have their tuition fees paid and can apply for an income-assessed NHS bursary (the exception being students training to be doctors or dentists who receive financial support from the NHS during the latter stages of their undergraduate studies only). Those not funded by the NHS are treated the same as other students in respect of student support. For further information about NHS bursaries – the occupations that qualify and other eligibility criteria, visit www.nhsbsa. nhs.uk/students.

Finally, most of the job titles listed in this section are protected by law and require you to register with an appropriate organisation in order to use that title and to practise in that role. Similarly, many of the health-related careers detailed here require you to undergo criminal record checks and to be in good health.

Biomedical scientist

Biomedical scientists work in hospital and other biomedical science laboratories. They investigate body tissues and fluids, using a wide range of methods of measurement and analysis. The majority of routine tests are performed by rapid, automated methods, leaving laboratory staff free to do more complex and demanding work using sophisticated technology.

There is a wide range of specialist fields. The main disciplines of biomedical science are:

- **clinical chemistry** – the chemical analysis of blood and other specimens

- **blood transfusion** – the identification of individual blood groups to assess compatibility of transfusions for patients; also the preparation of blood products ready for administering to patients

- **haematology** – the study of blood, including carrying out blood-cell counts for conditions such as anaemia and leukaemia, and investigating clotting defects

- **histopathology** – the preparation and study of tissue samples taken from patients during examinations, operations or during post-mortems, to identify abnormalities arising from circulatory and respiratory diseases, cancer etc

- **medical microbiology** – the study of micro-organisms such as viruses, bacteria, parasitic protozoa and fungi; the work involves culturing (i.e. growing in artificial conditions) organisms taken from patients, identifying the organisms and finding the most suitable antibiotics

- **immunology** – involves work on infectious diseases (such as AIDS), allergic reactions, tumour growth, organ transplants, tissue grafts and immune deficiency

- **cytopathology** – the study of disease in cells, including analysing samples taken in routine cancer-screening programmes

- **clinical/molecular genetics** – includes examining chromosomes for abnormalities, helping to identify pre-natal or other problems.

Most biomedical scientists are employed by the NHS in hospital laboratories. There are also employment opportunities in Health Protection Agency laboratories, private laboratories, pharmaceutical firms producing drugs and medicines, government departments, veterinary services, university research laboratories, forensic laboratories and in the medical sections of the Armed Forces.

Entry qualifications

To gain registration as a biomedical scientist you have to complete a biomedical science degree that has been approved by the Health Professions Council (HPC) – which includes those accredited by the Institute of Biomedical Science (IBMS) – and gain the award of certificate of competence (based on a portfolio of evidence built up in the workplace). For lists of HPC-approved and IBMS-accredited degree courses, see the HPC and IBMS websites listed below. There are some opportunities to work in a laboratory and to study part time for an HPC-approved/IBMS-accredited degree.

Biomedical scientists need be methodical, be able to concentrate for long periods and pay attention to detail. They also need to cope with work that can, at times, be routine and repetitive.

N.B. Training programmes and career structures for biomedical scientists are currently being revised, as part of the Modernising Scientific Careers programme. For information, search for 'Modernising Scientific Careers' at: www.dh.gov.uk.

Training and career development

Biomedical science is a rapidly changing profession, and, increasingly, there are opportunities for people to take on additional responsibilities, and to move into specialist, advanced and consultant-equivalent roles. Some biomedical scientists move into management and training posts. The IBMS offers professional qualifications suitable for members who want to specialise in particular areas of biomedical science. There are also opportunities overseas.

Finding vacancies

Vacancies are advertised on the NHS Jobs website, and there is a link to job vacancies on the Institute of Biomedical Science's website.

While at university, or as a recent graduate, you can access information about potential employers and current graduate vacancies through your university careers service. Further information about the help that is available through university careers services is provided in Chapter three.

Sources of further information

Health Professions Council (HPC) – tel: 020 7582 0866.
www.hpc-uk.org

Institute of Biomedical Science (IBMS) – tel: 020 7713 0214. www.ibms.org

NHS Careers – tel: 0345 60 60 655. www.nhscareers.nhs.uk

NHS Wales Careers – tel: 01443 233472. www.nhswalescareers.com

www.jobs.nhs.uk – the job vacancy website for NHS employers across England and Wales.

Clinical physiologist

Clinical physiologists use a variety of equipment and techniques to assess patients and measure how well their organs or body systems are functioning. In some cases they also give therapeutic treatments and care. Most clinical physiologists work in hospitals, as part of a medical or surgical team; some may work in community settings or visit patients in their homes.

There are various specialties that clinical physiologists can work in; some of the main roles are described below.

- **Audiologists** are concerned with hearing and balance. They prescribe and fit hearing aids and provide support for dealing with tinnitus, lack of balance and other similar conditions. N.B. a related job is that of audiological scientist. This is a more senior role and involves researching and developing new diagnosis techniques, interpreting clinical tests and taking on a managerial role within a hospital department. Clinical scientists (including audiological scientists) are described in more detail in Chapter six.

- **Cardiac physiologists** deal with patients with known, or suspected, heart disease. Work in this area involves, for example, measuring the electrical activity of the heart, monitoring the operation of heart pacemakers, analysing blood gases and measuring arterial pressure. Cardiac physiologists may also monitor heart function during operations.

- **Respiratory physiologists** work on measuring and assessing lung function. They deal with patients who are suffering breathing difficulties, chest pains, sleep disorders and so on. They may assess patients at rest and while exercising, undertake sleep studies, administer allergy tests and provide ventilation to patients on wards.

- **Clinical physiologists (neurophysiology)** are concerned with the nervous system. They use various equipment and techniques to measure electrical activity in the brain or neurological responses to stimuli, such as flashes of light. Clinical physiologists working in this area are responsible for diagnosing a range of neurological disorders, including epilepsy, strokes, multiple sclerosis and muscular dystrophy.

- **Gastrointestinal (GI) physiologists** assess and diagnose problems of the digestive tract and associated organs, such as the liver, pancreas and bile tract. GI physiologists deal with patients suffering from swallowing disorders, faecal incontinence, constipation or pelvic floor dysfunction, for example.

Other areas of work include clinical perfusion (see Chapter six for further details), critical care technology, ophthalmic science and vision science, sleep physiology, urodynamics and vascular technology.

Entry qualifications

Audiologists require either a degree or postgraduate qualification in audiology. Degree courses last four years and include one year on a clinical placement. Entry onto an MSc or postgraduate diploma course is possible for those with a first degree in a science subject, the most relevant of which are biological science subjects or physics.

To work in most other specialties requires a degree in clinical physiology. There are just a few full-time degree courses; these offer specific pathways in cardiology, respiratory physiology, neurophysiology or gastrointestinal physiology. The more typical route to qualifying is to start work in a hospital as a trainee and take a degree in clinical physiology on a part-time basis.

Clinical physiologists in all specialties need good communication skills and the ability to put patients at their ease. They also need to be able to maintain accurate and thorough records. Teamwork is also important, as the work involves close interaction with doctors and other healthcare staff.

Training and career development

Once in employment, training is on the job. You may be expected to attend short courses and seminars in order to keep up to date with developments in your specialty. The Registration Council for Clinical Physiologists currently holds a voluntary register of practitioners.

Clinical physiologists can work their way up to consultant or senior management levels. Positions at the higher grades may involve managing a team and training junior staff or, possibly, undertaking research.

N.B. Training programmes and career structures for clinical physiologists are currently being revised, as part of the Modernising Scientific Careers programme. For information, search for 'Modernising Scientific Careers' at: www.dh.gov.uk.

Finding vacancies

Vacancies for trainees are advertised on the NHS Jobs website, in the local press and in Jobcentre Plus offices. Jobs may also be advertised via some of the professional bodies listed below.

While at university, or as a recent graduate, you can access information about potential employers and current graduate vacancies through your university careers service. Further information about the help that is available through university careers services is provided in Chapter three.

Sources of further information

Association for Respiratory Technology & Physiology – tel: 0845 226 3062. www.artp.org.uk

Association of Gastrointestinal Physiology – part of the British Society of Gastroenterology. www.bsg.org

Association of Neurophysiological Scientists – www.ansuk.org

British Academy of Audiology – tel: 01625 504066. www.baaudiology.org

NHS Careers – tel: 0345 60 60 655. www.nhscareers.nhs.uk

NHS Wales Careers – tel: 01443 233472. www.nhswalescareers.com

The Registration Council for Clinical Physiologists – tel: 0845 226 3064. www.rccp.co.uk

The Society for Cardiological Science & Technology – tel: 0845 838 6037. www.scst.org.uk

www.jobs.nhs.uk – the job vacancy website for NHS employers across England and Wales

Dentist

The role of a dentist involves preventing and treating dental and oral diseases, correcting dental malformations and treating dental and facial injuries. There are opportunities to work a variety of settings, as described below. Dentists may also move into university teaching and research work. All dentists must be registered with the General Dental Council.

In **general practice**, a dentist's responsibilities vary from patient to patient – they may undertake a routine check-up, fit dentures, treat an emergency case, apply crowns, give a filling or extract teeth. They also give advice to patients about how to care for their teeth, and refer patients on for hospital treatment, if required. Dentists in general practice can choose to treat NHS or private patients; often they work with both.

Dentists working for **hospital dental services** perform the more complex procedures that are not possible in general practice. They may also choose to specialise in areas such as orthodontics, paediatric dentistry, oral and maxillofacial surgery and restorative dentistry.

Dentists working in **community dental services** work with particular groups of patients, such as children, older people and people with disabilities. Community dentists may be based in central clinics, but also run screening programmes in schools, or provide care through mobile surgeries.

In **industry**, a few major companies employ dentists in salaried posts as a benefit to their staff – although these posts are relatively uncommon and may involve part-time work.

Dentists in the **Armed Forces** are employed as officers and provide dental care to all service personnel and their families, in the UK and on overseas bases. As a member of the Armed Forces, dentists must be committed to all aspects of service life as well as their dental profession.

Entry qualifications

To work as a dentist you need to take a degree course in dentistry leading to BDS or BChD. Undergraduate courses last five years, or six – if you need to supplement your scientific knowledge through a 'pre-dental year'. Four-year courses are available for graduates who already have a relevant degree in a biomedical science or a health professional qualification.

The personal qualities required to work as a dentist include a caring and reassuring manner and the ability to work under pressure. You also need to be able to deal with all kinds of people, some of whom may be anxious or in pain, or who have let their teeth get into a bad state. The work requires a high level of manual dexterity, the ability to concentrate and good eyesight. Particularly in general practice, dentists need business and team leadership skills.

Training and career development

After graduating, dentists usually undertake a two-year general professional training (GPT) programme. GPT includes training in all types of settings, but the exact structure of your training will vary depending on whether you plan to work in general practice, the community dental service or the hospital dental service. For those wanting to work in the community or in general practice, your GPT must include one year of supervised vocational training (VT). For newly qualified dentists wanting to work in the hospital dental service, GPT will include a structured introduction to junior hospital posts in a variety of specialties. To become a specialist in a particular aspect of dentistry, such as orthodontics, requires further training and study.

Dentists in general practice usually start work as an associate (i.e. self-employed) or assistant in an established practice. With experience, it may be possible to become a partner in a practice or to set up your own practice. Experienced dentists in general practice may undergo additional training in order to work as 'Dentists with Special Interests' (DwSIs). For example, they may specialise in treating injuries and diseases affecting the tooth root, straightening teeth, minor operations and so on.

Dentists in the community dental service may start their careers as community clinical dental officers (CCDO). With experience and further postgraduate qualifications, they may progress to the level of senior dental officer (SDO).

Dentists who wish to work in the hospital dental service specialising in oral and maxillo-facial surgery need to undertake a medical degree, in addition to a degree in dentistry.

Finding vacancies

All NHS organisations in England and Wales advertise their vacancies on the NHS jobs website, www.jobs.nhs.uk and in the local press. Jobs are also advertised in the BDJ (the British Dental Journal), which is available to members of the British Dental Association (BDA), and on the BDA's dedicated jobs website, www.bdjjobs.co.uk.

While at university, or as a recent graduate, you can access information about potential employers and current graduate vacancies through your university careers service. Further information about the help that is available through university careers services is provided in Chapter three.

Sources of further information

British Dental Association – tel: 020 7935 0875. www.bda.org

General Dental Council – tel: 0845 22 4141. www.gdc-uk.org

NHS Careers – tel: 0345 60 60 655. www.nhscareers.nhs.uk

NHS Wales Careers – tel: 01443 233472. www.nhswalescareers.com

Dietitian

Dietitians deal with the science of nutrition, as well as with the social and psychological reasons behind our eating habits. Dietitians need to know why different nutrients are needed and which foods contain them. They must be interested in science, but also able to communicate with and motivate people about changing their diets, without being judgmental.

Most dietitians work in the NHS either in hospitals, community settings or special units, such as those specialising in patients with metabolic diseases; opportunities also exist in private healthcare. The work involves dealing with people who have particular dietary requirements due to conditions such as kidney disease, cancer, diabetes or allergies. Patients may have eating disorders or depression, or their appetite may have been affected by medication. Some patients may be recovering from surgery and have trouble swallowing and therefore absorbing all the nutrients they need; other patients may not be able to feed themselves, such as those in intensive care.

The dietitian plans appropriate diets, monitors their effectiveness and offers advice to patients and other healthcare professionals, such as doctors, nurses and health visitors. They may also help to create hospital food policies. In addition, dietitians undertake health promotion activities, helping groups or individuals to consider their diet afresh and to change their eating habits before they develop weight problems or become ill.

Other fields of work include advising on catering (in the school meals service, in residential schools, colleges etc); working with food manufacturers (advising on ingredients, dealing with consumers' enquiries and producing information about products) and in sports nutrition. Writing books and articles and, perhaps, working in television and radio, lecturing and/or researching in colleges and universities are other possibilities.

Entry qualifications

To work as a dietitian, you must be registered with the Health Professions Council (HPC), having taken an HPC-approved degree or postgraduate course in dietetics, or in human nutrition and dietetics. The HPC's website lists approved courses as does the NHS Careers website. Approved postgraduate qualifications are open to people whose first degree course includes sufficient study of nutrition, human physiology or biochemistry.

This type of work demands that you are able to get on with, and motivate, all sorts of different people. It's also important that you can communicate complex ideas simply and effectively. Empathy and compassion are critical, as for all healthcare professions.

Training and career development

You need to undertake continuing professional development (CPD) to maintain your HPC registration, which may involve attending short courses, conferences etc to keep up to date with developments in this field. With experience, and further training, dietitians can specialise in areas such as working with children or cancer patients. There is a clear promotion structure within the NHS, to consultant or management level.

Finding vacancies

All NHS organisations in England and Wales advertise their vacancies on the NHS jobs website, www.jobs.nhs.uk and in the local press. Jobs are also advertised in the monthly journal *Dietetics Today*, which is available to members of the British Dietetic Association (BDA), and on the BDA's dedicated jobs website www.bdacareerchoices.com.

While at university, or as a recent graduate, you can access information about potential employers and current graduate vacancies through your university careers service. Further information about the help that is available through university careers services is provided in Chapter three.

Sources of further information

British Dietetic Association (BDA) – tel: 0121 200 8080.
www.bda.uk.com

Health Professions Council (HPC) – tel: 020 7582 0866. www.hpc-uk.org

NHS Careers – tel: 0345 60 60 655. www.nhscareers.nhs.uk

NHS Wales Careers – tel: 01443 233472. www.nhswalescareers.com

Doctor

Doctors diagnose medical conditions and treat patients; they also observe and monitor patients' progress, provide advice and promote good health. It is a highly responsible job, and can be stressful. The training is long and difficult, so you need to be completely committed to medicine as a career.

The main opportunities for doctors are in the following areas of work.

- **General practice** – doctors who work as general practitioners (GPs) provide primary care to patients who present with a wide range of conditions. They deal with both the physical and mental health of patients of all ages, although much of their time is concerned with child health, maternity care, conditions relating to old age and preventive medicine. Where necessary, GPs refer patients on to specialists. Most doctors work in partnership with other GPs, leading a team that may include a practice manager, community nurses, midwives, health visitors, social workers, administrators and receptionists.

- **Hospital work** – doctors work in a wide range of medical and surgical specialties, dealing with referrals from GPs and emergency admissions. A consultant is responsible for a team of doctors, including junior doctors still in training. Specialties include, for example, anaesthetics, cardiology, cardiothoracic surgery, geriatric medicine, neurology, neurosurgery, paediatric surgery, palliative medicine and rheumatology.

- **Community health** – doctors working in community-based services may specialise in areas such as child health, mental health, sexual health, and services for older people or for those with learning disabilities.

- **Public health** – this is concerned with health matters affecting whole populations. Doctors working in this field need a wide knowledge of medicine and a special expertise in epidemiology (the study of disease epidemics) and disease control. The work may involve researching the health of specific populations and developing healthcare programmes to tackle particular problems and inequalities between population groups.

- **Occupational medicine** – doctors can work in industry and commerce, particularly in those sectors that are associated with certain health problems. They may be involved in preventive medicine (reviewing health and safety arrangements or carrying out routine medical examinations, for example) or in treating people who have fallen ill due to work-related factors or who have been injured at work.

- **The Armed Forces** – doctors serving as medical officers in the Armed Forces often take on the role of GP for service personnel and their families. They may also be deployed on military operations, treating casualties in field hospitals, or specialise in public health/occupational medicine.

- **Medical research and teaching** – there are opportunities for medical graduates with, for example, the Medical Research Council, medical charities and in university medical schools.

All doctors must be registered with the General Medical Council.

Entry qualifications

To work as a doctor, you need to start with a degree in medicine. Undergraduate courses usually last five years. Some six-year courses are available, which include either a preliminary year for those who don't meet the standard entry criteria, or the option to gain a second degree through an extra year of study, known as an intercalated degree. Four-year courses are available for graduates who already have a relevant degree in a biomedical or life science.

As well as academic qualifications, doctors need a range of personal qualities including excellent communication skills, a caring and compassionate nature, flexibility, conscientiousness and self-motivation. An interest in people, as well as science, is critical too.

Training and career development

After graduating, trainee doctors undertake a two-year Foundation Programme, which allows them to experience a series of placements in a range of specialties and settings. At the end of the Foundation

Programme, doctors can opt to train as specialists (in medicine or surgery) or as GPs, although training places are limited and not everyone is successful in their application. Those who do not go into specialty training can apply for a position as a 'specialty grade doctor'.

GP training takes three years, and specialty training can take up to eight years, depending on the specialism. During training, doctors take the exams of the relevant professional body, such as The Royal College of Surgeons or The Royal College of Physicians.

GPs may work in single-handed or group practice or in a health centre. Many GPs develop their own particular areas of expertise. As a specialist, it is possible to work your way up to the level of consultant, the most senior post in a hospital department – responsible for treating patients, teaching and supervising staff, and managing the department.

Finding vacancies

All NHS organisations in England and Wales advertise their vacancies on the NHS jobs website, www.jobs.nhs.uk and in the local press. Jobs are also advertised in the *BMJ* (British Medical Journal) and its dedicated jobs website www.bmjcareers.com.

While at university, or as a recent graduate, you can access information about potential employers and current graduate vacancies through your university careers service. Further information about the help that is available through university careers services is provided in Chapter three.

Sources of further information

BMA (British Medical Association) – tel: 020 7387 4499. www.bma.org.uk

General Medical Council (GMC) – tel: 0845 357 8001. www.gmc-uk.org

NHS Careers – tel: 0345 60 60 655. www.nhscareers.nhs.uk

NHS Wales Careers – tel: 01443 233472. www.nhswalescareers.com

Just a few Royal College (professional body) websites are listed below.

www.rcoa.ac.uk – The Royal College of Anaesthetists

www.rcgp.org.uk – Royal College of General Practitioners

www.rcog.org.uk – Royal College of Obstetricians and Gynaecologists

www.rcpch.ac.uk – Royal College of Paediatrics and Child Health

www.rcpath.org - The Royal College of Pathologists

www.rcplondon.ac.uk - The Royal College of Physicians

www.rcpsych.ac.uk - The Royal College of Psychiatrists

www.rcr.ac.uk - The Royal College of Radiologists

www.rcseng.ac.uk - The Royal College of Surgeons of England

Midwife

Midwives work with women and their babies during pregnancy, labour, delivery and after birth.

Antenatal care: a pregnant woman first meets a midwife either in the antenatal clinic or in her own home, usually early in pregnancy. She has regular check-ups at the clinic with a midwife and/or doctor or obstetrician. They examine her to make sure that both she and her unborn baby are in good health, and that the baby is developing normally. The midwife is usually the main contact for the woman, and will liaise with the other health workers. The midwife will discuss with the woman the sort of birth she hopes to have, her attitudes towards high-tech equipment and different sorts of pain relief and will give advice on how the woman can maintain her own health and that of her baby. Midwives may also get involved in education for parenthood – teaching groups of women and men about labour and giving birth, and how to care for the baby in the early days.

Delivery: midwives acting on their own carry out normal deliveries of babies. When everything is straightforward, there is no doctor in attendance. But, of course, the midwife must be able to recognise the warning signs of possible problems, and know when a doctor needs to be called.

Postnatal care: midwives make sure the mother is recovering properly from the birth, and that the baby is in good health. Midwives advise on feeding the baby and on general baby care.

Once the mother is home, mother and baby are the community midwife's responsibility for at least ten days (sometimes up to 28 days) of the baby's life, before the health visitor takes over.

Midwives can work in the maternity units of large hospitals, in smaller hospitals that have midwife-led units for normal deliveries, in private maternity hospitals, in the community, for agencies, or as self-employed practitioners (independent midwives).

Community midwives work between a number of bases – hospitals, GP surgeries, health centres and antenatal clinics, and are often on the road between one home visit and the next.

Entry qualifications

Entry is through a degree in midwifery approved by the Nursing and Midwifery Council. The NHS Careers website lists details of all midwifery training programmes.

A midwife needs good communication and teamwork skills, to be caring, sensitive, observant and self-reliant, and to be able to keep calm and alert under pressure.

Training and career development

There are opportunities for promotion, and courses leading to advanced qualifications. There are also opportunities to specialise in the clinical or managerial fields, or to go into research or teaching.

For senior midwives who wish to progress their career yet continue to do practical work, midwife consultant posts have been developed. These involve spending part of the time working with clients and the rest of the time being involved in training and development, research etc.

Finding vacancies

You can search for job vacancies in the NHS through www.jobs.nhs.uk.

While at university, or as a recent graduate, you can access information about potential employers and current graduate vacancies through your university careers service. Further information about the help that is available through university careers services is provided in Chapter three.

Sources of further information

NHS Careers – tel: 0345 60 60 655. www.nhscareers.nhs.uk

NHS Wales Careers – tel: 01443 233472. www.nhswalescareers.com

Nursing & Midwifery Council – tel: 020 7333 9333. www.nmc-uk.org

The Royal College of Midwives – tel: 020 7312 3535. www.rcm.org.uk

Nurse

Nurses work as part of a healthcare team. They monitor and assess the physical, psychological and social needs of their patients, and plan and deliver the care required. Practical care may involve a wide range of tasks, varying from job to job. Nurses are trained for, and work in, a variety of settings – health centres, industry, schools, the community, homes for people who have learning disabilities or mental health problems, as well as hospitals. In hospitals, areas that nurses may work in include accident and emergency, acute wards, psychiatric wards, children's wards, operating theatres and intensive care. Providing nursing care can involve shift, weekend and public holiday duties.

You choose to train in one of four main branches or fields of practice:

- **adult nursing** – nursing people with a wide variety of illnesses or conditions

- **children's nursing** – nursing children from babyhood to adolescence

- **learning disabilities nursing** – nursing and caring for people of all ages who have a wide range of learning difficulties – the work may be based in a range of social settings

- **mental health nursing** – nursing and caring for people of all ages with mental health problems.

Most nurses work in the NHS but there are also opportunities for employment in private hospitals, with nursing agencies, with residential nursing homes, in the Armed Forces, and with charities such as those providing care for cancer patients, or undertaking overseas development and relief work.

Entry qualifications

Entry to nursing is through a degree or diploma in nursing, approved by the Nursing and Midwifery Council (NMC). From 2013, all students entering training will need to enter through a degree, which takes three years, full time. The NHS website lists details of all current nurse training programmes, including those aimed at graduates with relevant degrees. All practising nurses must be registered with the NMC.

If you have previous learning, such as a relevant degree, this can be accredited towards some of the nurse training programme requirements, which means you could complete nurse training in a shorter time. Up to one third of the three-year programme could be accredited.

Besides academic qualifications, a nurse needs good communication and observational skills, understanding, tact and sensitivity towards people, teamwork and problem-solving skills and the personality to remain calm when patients or their relatives may be anxious or distressed.

Training and career development

In all branches of nursing there are opportunities to move into management, research or nurse teaching. Nurse consultants may manage patient caseloads, train and develop staff, conduct research and run their own wards and budgets. Nurses may take further training to work in areas such as health visiting or district nursing.

Some continuing education courses for registered nurses lead to postgraduate-level qualifications. All nurses have to meet post-registration education and practice (PREP) requirements in order to maintain their registration with the NMC.

Finding vacancies

You can search for job vacancies in the NHS through www.jobs.nhs.uk. Nursing jobs are also advertised in the *Nursing Times* (or see the website www.nursingtimes.net) and can be accessed through the Royal College of Nursing's website www.rcn.org.uk.

While at university, or as a recent graduate, you can access information about potential employers and current graduate vacancies through your university careers service. Further information about the help that is available through university careers services is provided in Chapter three.

Sources of further information

NHS Careers – tel: 0345 60 60 655. www.nhscareers.nhs.uk

NHS Wales Careers – tel: 01443 233472. www.nhswalescareers.com

Nursing & Midwifery Council (NMC) – tel: 020 7333 9333. www.nmc-uk.org

Nutritionist

Nutritionists are scientists who study the way nutrients are used in the body and investigate the relationship between diet and disease. They do not have direct patient contact unless they are working under the supervision of a registered health professional, such as a dietitian. Instead, they work in health promotion roles, in research and development, and as industry consultants. As such, the range of potential employers is vast, and nutritional science is a rapidly developing area.

Depending on your particular interests, it is possible to specialise in a number of different aspects of nutrition. There are currently several government-backed initiatives promoting healthy eating, for example, to improve nutrition among young children, which offer opportunities for public health nutritionists, typically working in Primary Care Trusts or government departments. Charities, food retailers and food manufacturers may also offer similar positions. The food and drink industry also employs nutritionists in product development, as do animal feed manufacturers. Within the sport and exercise sector, there are opportunities for nutritionists to work directly with elite athletes and with members of the general public, helping them improve their sporting performance through diet. Research posts with universities and research institutes offer opportunities to study the many different branches of nutritional science.

Entry qualifications

Entry into this area of work requires a degree or postgraduate qualification in nutrition, public health nutrition or a related subject. Suitable degree subjects for entry onto postgraduate courses include biochemistry, human biology, food science, physiology, pharmacy, medicine etc. The Association for Nutrition accredits certain undergraduate and postgraduate courses that lead to direct entry onto the UK Voluntary Register of Nutritionists. (In the past, accreditation was through the Nutrition Society, which some literature may still reference.)

In general, nutritionists need to be analytical and good at interpreting scientific data. Communication and organisational skills are important as is the ability to work to deadlines. Some roles require laboratory skills.

Training and career development

Specific training will vary according to the exact nature of your employment and is likely to involve short courses, conferences, etc. Registered nutritionists are required to undertake continuing professional development (CPD) throughout their careers.

For those with relevant qualifications and experience, there are opportunities to work overseas, aiding emergency relief operations or working on projects in developing countries. It may be possible to undertake a postgraduate qualification such as a masters degree or even a PhD, on a part-time basis, while in employment. These may be required for more senior posts.

Finding vacancies

All NHS organisations in England and Wales advertise their vacancies on the NHS jobs website, www.jobs.nhs.uk and in the local press. The Nutrition Society advertises jobs on its website. Employers may also advertise vacancies on their own websites or through specialist recruitment agencies and online job sites.

While at university, or as a recent graduate, you can access information about potential employers and current graduate vacancies through your university careers service. Further information about the help that is available through university careers services is provided in Chapter three.

Sources of further information

Association for Nutrition – tel: 078 0110 6451. www.associationfornutrition.org

NHS Careers – tel: 0345 60 60 655. www.nhscareers.nhs.uk

NHS Wales Careers – tel: 01443 233472. www.nhswalescareers.com

The Nutrition Society – tel: 020 7602 0228. www.nutritionsociety.org

Nutritionists in Industry – www.nii.org.uk

The Sport and Exercise Nutrition Register – tel 0121 200 8080. www.senr.org.uk

Optometrist

Optometrists examine eyes, test sight and prescribe (and sometimes fit) spectacles or contact lenses for those who need them. They give advice on visual problems and check for any eye disease, signs of injury or abnormality. Other general health problems can also be identified through examinations of the eye, such as diabetes and high blood pressure. If necessary, optometrists refer patients to a medical specialist. They may share, with a medical practitioner, responsibility for the care of patients with long-term eye problems.

There are several well-known chains of opticians that employ optometrists; some offer franchise opportunities for those wanting to run their own business. It is also possible to set up your own practice and work independently, as a sole practitioner or as a partnership. There are opportunities in hospital departments or clinics, or in research and teaching. As a qualified optometrist, it is possible to specialise in areas such as paediatrics, low vision and sports vision.

Entry qualifications

To work as an optometrist you need to be registered with the General Optical Council (GOC). As a first step towards registration, you need to gain at least a second class degree in optometry from an institution approved by the GOC.

Optometrists deal with people of all ages and backgrounds and need good communication skills and a caring manner. Manual dexterity and practical skills are required to use the various types of examination equipment. Some aspects of the work are repetitive; therefore, an ability to remain accurate and pay good attention to detail is required. Work in private practice requires good commercial and business skills.

Training and career development

After graduating, optometry graduates must complete a pre-registration period of training under the supervision of a qualified optometrist. This involves work-based assessments, and is followed by a 'Final Assessment' examination, leading to registration with the GOC. The College of Optometrists offers higher qualifications in a range of specialist subject areas, such as glaucoma and orthoptics. Optometrists must keep their skills and knowledge up to date throughout their career.

Optometrists in the NHS can work their way up to consultant or senior management levels. Positions at the higher grades may involve managing a team and training junior staff or, possibly, undertaking research.

Finding vacancies

All NHS organisations in England and Wales advertise their vacancies on the NHS jobs website, www.jobs.nhs.uk and in the local press. Jobs are also advertised in the journal *Optician* and on its associated website, www.opticianonline.net.

While at university, or as a recent graduate, you can access information about potential employers and current graduate vacancies through your university careers service. Further information about the help that is available through university careers services is provided in Chapter three.

Sources of further information

Association of Optometrists – tel: 020 7261 9661. www.aop.org.uk

The College of Optometrists – tel: 020 7839 6000. www.college-optometrists.org

General Optical Council (GOC) – tel: 020 7580 3898. www.optical.org

NHS Careers – tel: 0345 60 60 655. www.nhscareers.nhs.uk

NHS Wales Careers – tel: 01443 233472. www.nhswalescareers.com

Orthoptist

Orthoptists diagnose and treat defects of vision and abnormalities of eye movement. Patients may have problems such as a lazy eye, a squint or double vision. The orthoptist's job is to assess the patient's vision and ocular alignment in order to diagnose the condition and decide on the most suitable treatment. Orthoptic treatments including fitting eye patches, advising on exercises or recommending the use of glasses. Orthoptists refer patients on to an ophthalmologist (eye surgeon) if surgery is required, but remain involved with the patient monitoring their progress after their operation.

Ocular problems affect people of all ages, but about half of the patients that orthoptists deal with are children. For example, orthoptists may conduct pre-school vision screening for four- and five-year-olds. Many child patients have physical or learning disabilities, sometimes both. Orthoptists also work with adults, particularly with older people. In these cases, ocular problems are often as a result of a stroke, glaucoma and or age-related macula degeneration.

Most orthoptists work in eye hospitals or specialist departments within large, general hospitals. Some work in community settings, others in education, training or research.

Entry qualifications

To work as an orthoptist, you must be registered with the Health Professions Council (HPC), having taken an HPC-approved degree course. There are two approved degree courses in orthoptics – at the Universities of Liverpool and Sheffield.

Orthoptists need to have good interpersonal skills in order to put people at their ease and, in the case of young children, to maintain their interest and cooperation. Orthoptists also need to be accurate and observant. Self-motivation and the ability to work alone and as part of a team are important.

Training and career development

Degree courses combine academic theory with hands-on training, gained through practical sessions at university and placements in hospitals and community settings. Once in employment, it may be possible to gain a postgraduate qualification, such as an MSc or PhD, on a part-time basis. These may be required for more senior posts.

The NHS offers a structured career path, leading to the role of head orthoptist, in charge of an orthoptic department with responsibility for managing and training junior staff. There are opportunities for orthoptists to become specialists in dealing with conditions such as cataracts, or to work abroad or for private healthcare providers.

Finding vacancies

All NHS organisations in England and Wales advertise their vacancies on the NHS jobs website, www.jobs.nhs.uk and in the local press.

While at university, or as a recent graduate, you can access information about potential employers and current graduate vacancies through your university careers service. Further information about the help that is available through university careers services is provided in Chapter three.

Sources of further information

British and Irish Orthoptic Society – tel: 020 7387 7992. www.orthoptics.org.uk

Health Professions Council (HPC) – tel: 020 7582 0866. www.hpc-uk.org

NHS Careers – tel: 0345 60 60 655. www.nhscareers.nhs.uk

NHS Wales Careers – tel: 01443 233472. www.nhswalescareers.com

University of Liverpool – Directorate of Orthoptics and Vision Science. Tel: 0151 794 5731. www.liv.ac.uk/orthoptics

The University of Sheffield – Academic Unit of Ophthalmology and Orthoptics. Tel: 0114 271 2713. www.sheffield.ac.uk/medicine/orthoptics

Pharmacist

Pharmacists are responsible for supervising the dispensing of medicines prescribed by doctors. Their role requires them to be experts in the chemical composition of drugs, the range of effects they have and how they interact with other medications. Pharmacists therefore check and control what is being prescribed and are legally responsible for any mistakes. There are various branches of pharmacy and the exact nature of the pharmacist's role varies accordingly.

- **Community pharmacists** – over half of all pharmacists work in community settings. Some are employed by health centres, but most work in retail outlets – on the high street, in supermarkets and so on. As well as dispensing medicines, retail pharmacies sell many other products, such as toiletries, cosmetics and baby food, so the role of the pharmacist may extend to managing retail operations. Community pharmacists offer advice to patients about the proper use of their medicines, possible side effects and common ailments. They also provide specialist services, such as providing medicines to nursing homes.

- **Hospital pharmacists** – many pharmacists work in hospitals, supplying medicines to inpatients and outpatients. They take part in ward rounds with the consultants, interviewing patients to find out about any medications they have been taking. The pharmacist also oversees production of certain medicines that need to be manufactured on-site. Some hospitals run quality assurance laboratories, which offer a service to other local hospitals, in order to check the quality of the medicines they are using. These laboratories employ pharmacists, who are assisted by scientific officers and technicians.

- **Industrial pharmacists** – opportunities exist with pharmaceutical companies and the manufacturers of veterinary products to work in research and development (formulating new medicines or improving existing ones) or in production management, overseeing the mass-production of pharmaceutical products.

- **Other opportunities** – pharmacists can work in a number of other settings, such as in prisons, the Armed Forces, pharmaceutical wholesalers and agricultural and veterinary pharmacies. Locum pharmacists provide temporary cover for holidays etc – working as a locum is a popular option for people looking for occasional work.

Entry qualifications

You need to take an accredited degree course in pharmacy, leading to the qualification MPharm (Master of Pharmacy), as a first step towards becoming a pharmacist. The General Pharmaceutical Council (GPhC) will accredit courses and maintain the register of qualified pharmacists from 2010 - a precise date has yet to be confirmed. Until that time, accreditation will be through the Royal Pharmaceutical Society of Great Britain (RPSGB), which some literature may still reference.

Pharmacists need excellent communication skills - much of their role involves consulting with patients, as well as giving them advice and reassurance. Attention to detail and accuracy are essential qualities for this type of work. Community pharmacists also need business skills and the ability to manage a team of staff.

Training and career development

After graduating, trainee pharmacists must undertake a year of pre-registration training with an approved provider, either in a community or hospital pharmacy. At the end of this period, trainees must pass the RPSGB's registration exam and become members of the RPSGB in order to qualify and practise as pharmacists.

It is possible for qualified pharmacists to train as supplementary prescribers, meaning they can make any necessary changes to a doctor's or dentist's prescription, within certain boundaries. As an extension to this role, pharmacists can also train as independent prescribers, allowing them to be more responsive to their own caseload of patients.

There is a structured career path for pharmacists working within the NHS. It is also possible to move into a strategic role as a primary care pharmacist, with responsibility for planning local services and managing prescribing budgets and prescriber training. Pharmacists working in retail settings or industry may have opportunities to progress to senior management levels. Some pharmacists move into teaching, lecturing, academic research or journalism.

Finding vacancies

All NHS organisations in England and Wales advertise their vacancies on the NHS jobs website, www.jobs.nhs.uk and in the local press. Vacancies are also listed in the journal *Chemist+Druggist* and its associated website, www.chemistanddruggistjobs.co.uk. Employers may also advertise vacancies on their own websites or through specialist recruitment agencies and online job sites.

While at university, or as a recent graduate, you can access information about potential employers and current graduate vacancies through your university careers service. Further information about the help that is available through university careers services is provided in Chapter three.

Sources of further information

Association of the British Pharmaceutical Industry – tel: 0870 890 4333. www.abpi.org.uk and www.abpi-careers.org.uk

The General Pharmaceutical Council (GPhC) – tel: 020 3365 3400. www.pharmacyregulation.org

National Pharmacy Association – tel: 01727 858687. www.npa.co.uk

NHS Careers – tel: 0345 60 60 655. www.nhscareers.nhs.uk

NHS Wales Careers – tel: 01443 233472. www.nhswalescareers.com

Royal Pharmaceutical Society of Great Britain (RPSGB) – tel: 020 7735 9141. www.rpsgb.org.uk and www.pharmacycareers.org.uk

Physiotherapist

Most physiotherapists work in the NHS where they deal with patients who are suffering a loss of movement due to illness, injury or ageing – and particularly those conditions that affect the muscles, bones, heart, circulation and lungs. Patients may be unable to get about, wash, dress and feed themselves, clean the house or go to work. By devising a suitable programme of treatment, physiotherapists help patients regain their independence.

The physiotherapist first assesses the patient's problem by comparing the weaknesses and deficiencies in their movements with normal levels of activity. A treatment programme may then involve manual therapy, electrical treatments, water therapy or massage. The physiotherapist also teaches the patient exercises to loosen stiff joints, strengthen weak muscles and coordinate their movements.

In the NHS, physiotherapists frequently work with stroke victims and people who are permanently disabled to help them reach their full potential for movement, or with patients immediately after an operation. There are many other situations where physiotherapy may be used, such as in the care of older people; in specialist units (such as orthopaedics); with children in their own homes, or in hospitals or schools for children with disabilities; with expectant and new mothers in antenatal clinics and maternity units/hospitals; and in health education and promotion. Outside the NHS, physiotherapists can find work in private practice, either self-employed or as a member of staff in a private clinic. Other opportunities include working for sports clubs, health spas, gyms and so on. Some industrial or business organisations employ physiotherapists to help prevent and minimise workplace injuries caused through physical tasks, and to provide assessment and treatment to employees. Another employment option for physiotherapists is with those voluntary organisations that support people with particular illnesses or disabilities, such as multiple sclerosis.

Entry qualifications

To work as a physiotherapist, you must be registered with the Health Professions Council (HPC), having taken an HPC-approved degree or postgraduate course. The Council's website lists approved courses as does the NHS Careers website. Applicants should visit a physiotherapy department, e.g. at an open day, to observe the work prior to application or interview. Relevant work experience or voluntary work can be very helpful.

Physiotherapists require excellent communication skills and the ability to get on with people from all kinds of backgrounds. They also need to be highly observant and happy to work in a team of other health professionals, including doctors, nurses, social workers, occupational therapists etc. Empathy and compassion are critical, as for all health-related careers.

Training and career development

You need to undertake continuing professional development (CPD) to maintain your HPC registration, which may involve attending short courses, conferences etc to keep up to date with developments in this field. With experience, and further training, physiotherapists can specialise in treating particular client groups or conditions. There is a clear promotion structure within the NHS, to management or consultant level.

Finding vacancies

All NHS organisations in England and Wales advertise their vacancies on the NHS jobs website, www.jobs.nhs.uk and in the local press. Jobs are also advertised on the Chartered Society of Physiotherapy's dedicated jobs website, www.jobescalator.com and in its fortnightly magazine, *Frontline*, available on subscription.

While at university, or as a recent graduate, you can access information about potential employers and current graduate vacancies through your university careers service. Further information about the help that is available through university careers services is provided in Chapter three.

Sources of further information

The Chartered Society of Physiotherapy – tel: 020 7306 6666. www.csp.org.uk

Health Professions Council (HPC) – tel: 020 7582 0866. www.hpc-uk.org

NHS Careers – tel: 0345 60 60 655. www.nhscareers.nhs.uk

NHS Wales Careers – tel: 01443 233472. www.nhswalescareers.com

Radiographer

There are two branches of radiography in the health service – diagnostic radiography and radiotherapy radiography. You need to decide which aspect of radiography you wish to work in from the outset, as there are separate training routes for both, starting with your choice of degree.

Diagnostic radiographers use various techniques to produce images that can be used to diagnose diseases, injuries or other conditions. For example, they may operate X-ray machines, CT (computed tomography) scanners, MRI (magnetic resonance imaging) and ultrasound equipment. They may use nuclear medicine to introduce radioactive tracers into particular organs to show how they are working, or use specific techniques such as fluoroscopy, to image the digestive system, or angiography, to look at blood vessels.

Diagnostic radiography is the larger of the two branches of radiography, with opportunities to work in the radiology and imaging departments of many different hospitals, large and small. Diagnostic radiographers may also use mobile units to visit wards and operating theatres, or work in other hospital departments, such as antenatal or accident and emergency units. Often there is a rapid turnover of patients, and diagnostic radiographers rarely meet their patients more than once. The job may involve working shifts to provide 24-hour cover.

Radiotherapy radiographers, sometimes known as therapeutic radiographers, plan and deliver radiation treatments for patients suffering from cancer. This involves using an X-ray or scan to identify the exact location of the affected area, before calculating the dose required and the precise positioning of the radiation beam. The radiographer works in consultation with medical physicists and doctors.

Therapeutic radiographers can get to know individual patients quite well, as often regular treatment is required, for example, every day for five weeks. Weekend work is sometimes required to provide continuity of treatment, but generally work follows typical daytime hours, Monday to Friday.

Entry qualifications

Radiographers need to be registered with the Health Professions Council (HPC), having taken an HPC-approved degree course in either diagnostic radiography or radiotherapy/therapeutic radiography. There are a few accelerated courses for graduates who already have at least a second class degree in a relevant subject, such as biology or a health-related subject.

In general, radiographers need an interest in various aspects of science, such as anatomy, physiology, physics and biology, as well as in technology. They must have good communication and interpersonal skills, particularly in order to deal sympathetically with patients who may be anxious or in great discomfort or pain. The work also requires good observation skills and attention to detail.

Training and career development

The NHS has a structured career path and, with the necessary skills and additional qualifications, it is possible to gain promotion to the level of advanced practitioner, or even consultant radiographer. There are opportunities to specialise in particular aspects of either diagnostic or radiotherapy radiography. There are also positions in private health clinics and hospitals, in radiography education departments and in research. There are opportunities to work abroad.

Finding vacancies

All NHS organisations in England and Wales advertise their vacancies on the NHS jobs website, www.jobs.nhs.uk and in the local press. Jobs are also advertised in *Synergy News*, a journal published by the Society of Radiographers (SCoR).

While at university, or as a recent graduate, you can access information about potential employers and current graduate vacancies through your university careers service. Further information about the help that is available through university careers services is provided in Chapter three.

Sources of further information

Health Professions Council (HPC) – tel: 020 7582 0866. www.hpc-uk.org

NHS Careers – tel: 0345 60 60 655. www.nhscareers.nhs.uk

NHS Wales Careers – tel: 01443 233472. www.nhswalescareers.com

The Society of Radiographers (SCoR) – tel: 020 7740 7200. www.sor.org and www.radiographycareers.co.uk

Veterinary surgeon

Vets care for animals – preventing, diagnosing and treating diseases and injuries. Vets are trained to deal with a wide range of animal species, so have an in-depth knowledge of a variety of medical treatments and surgical techniques. There are opportunities for vets to work in a number of different settings, depending on their particular interests.

General practice – vets may work in single-handed practices or in partnership with other vets. They care for the general health of animals and advise on breeding matters. Practices in towns and cities tend to work predominantly with family pets. In rural areas, there are opportunities to specialise in the care of farm livestock and horses. Vets in general practice may also be involved in the care of birds and animals from zoos and animal parks, and with injured wildlife. Alongside their work in caring for animals, vets in general practice usually manage a team of staff including receptionists and veterinary nurses, and are responsible for managing all aspects of the business.

Government agencies – Defra (the Department for Environment, Food and Rural affairs) oversees a number of agencies that are concerned with animal matters, including Animal Health, the Veterinary Laboratories Agency, the Veterinary Medicines Directorate and the Food Standards Agency. The work may involve preventing and controlling outbreaks of epidemic diseases, checking on the welfare of livestock, researching animal diseases, regulating veterinary medicines, or enforcing laws relating to abattoirs and so on.

Research – as well as the Government's Veterinary Laboratories Agency, mentioned above, vets are employed by research institutes and universities to undertake animal-related research. Others work in industry, researching new drugs, animal feed, pet foods, livestock development etc. This type of work may involve experiments on animals.

Other employers – a small number of vets work as officers in the Royal Army Veterinary Corps. There are also salaried posts with animal welfare organisations, such as the RSPCA and PDSA.

The work can involve being on-call overnight and at weekends, travelling to and working in all manner of surroundings, some of which may be dirty or outdoors. Vets need to be alert to signs of abuse or cruelty.

Entry qualifications

To work as a vet, you must be registered with the Royal College of Veterinary Surgeons (RCVS) having taken an RCVS-approved degree in veterinary science or veterinary medicine.

Vets need to care about the welfare of animals, without being too sentimental. They also need to be good at dealing with people, self-confident and highly motivated. Vets working with large animals, in particular, need to be physically fit.

Training and career development

Vets are expected to keep their skills and knowledge up to date through continuous professional development (CPD). This may involve attending short courses, conferences and so on. The RCVS offers a programme of CPD particularly aimed at recent graduates.

The RCVS offers postgraduate qualifications, including a Certificate in Advanced Veterinary Practice. Vets can also take postgraduate courses to train to become specialists in areas such as anaesthetics, pathology and cardiology.

Finding vacancies

The BVA (British Veterinary Association) advertises vacancies in its journal *Veterinary Record*, and on its associated website www.vetrecordjobs.com. Jobs with government agencies may be advertised through the dedicated Civil Service recruitment website, www.civilservice.gov.uk/jobs. Employers may also advertise vacancies on their own websites or through specialist recruitment agencies and online job sites.

While at university, or as a recent graduate, you can access information about potential employers and current graduate vacancies through your university careers service. Further information about the help that is available through university careers services is provided in Chapter three.

Sources of further information

BVA (British Veterinary Association) – tel: 020 7636 6541. www.bva.co.uk

Royal College of Veterinary Surgeons (RCVS) – tel: 020 7222 2001. www.rcvs.org.uk/careers and www.walksoflife.org.uk

Chapter eight

Engineering careers

"Engineering can be a dangerous game..."

SOFTWARE ENGINEER

If you are interested in maths and science, particularly the physical sciences, and have yet to decide on your degree subject, you may want to consider engineering.

Engineering is all about designing, developing and creating a great variety of systems, products and environments, from microchips to bridges! There are many different fields of engineering. This chapter introduces you to some of the main specialist engineering careers:

- aerospace/aeronautical engineer
- chemical engineer
- civil engineer

- clinical engineer
- computer engineer
- design engineer
- electrical engineer
- electronics engineer
- mechanical engineer
- production engineer.

The engineering industry in the UK needs skilled and qualified employees, and is trying to encourage more young people – as well as women and people from ethnic minority backgrounds – to enter engineering. If you are still at school, there are various schemes to encourage young people to consider an engineering career, including taster courses and special projects. You might keep an eye out for such opportunities.

Aerospace/Aeronautical engineer

Aerospace and aeronautical engineers work on aircraft, satellites, weapons systems and space vehicles. They may be involved in research and development, testing, manufacturing, maintenance and repair.

Aerospace/aeronautical engineers work for aircraft manufacturers, individual airlines and aircraft maintenance companies, in research establishments, for organisations involved in air transport operations, and government departments. There are opportunities to work on both the military and the civilian side of the aerospace industry.

There is a wide range of roles, and aerospace/aeronautical engineers usually specialise in a particular area of work, such as hydraulics, engines or fuel systems. For example, hundreds of engineers work on a new aircraft during its design and development. Each engineer will be in a team involved with one particular section or system in the aircraft. Big issues currently facing research and development staff are fuel efficiency, using 'greener' fuels and reducing noise and air pollution.

In manufacturing, engineers oversee the production processes. Manufacturing firms often work in collaboration with other aerospace firms both in this country and abroad. Some firms specialise in the manufacture of particular aircraft components, such as Rolls-Royce which manufactures engines. Engineers may also manage maintenance, repair and overhaul programs, or be involved in accident investigation.

Chemical engineer

Chemical engineers develop and operate industrial processes that turn raw chemical materials into a wide variety of products ranging from fuels and plastics through to healthcare products and cosmetics. Chemical engineers are therefore employed in a range of industries, particularly in the energy, water, plastics, pharmaceutical, food and healthcare industries.

Chemical engineers may be involved in research, development and manufacturing operations. Those undertaking research develop new ideas for products, or new manufacturing processes, and need to be creative and innovative. They may work alongside industrial chemists. Chemical engineers involved in product or process development undertake testing, initially on a small scale, then designing how the product or process could be scaled up for full-scale manufacturing, and arranging for the machinery (plant) that will be used in the production process to be put in place.

Chemical engineers that work in production make sure that the manufacturing processes are operating effectively and efficiently, and product quality is maintained.

Whatever their role, chemical engineers need to be mindful of safety, cost effectiveness and environmental considerations, including the safe disposal or re-use of by-products and waste.

Civil engineer

Civil engineers are involved in the design and construction of a wide range of structures including tunnels, bridges, skyscrapers, stadiums, dams, industrial plants, flood defences and transport systems.

Civil engineers may be involved in all stages of a project. Consulting civil engineers are employed to undertake the design work. They have to take into consideration factors such as the stresses and loads the structure will need to withstand, the materials to be used, environmental considerations, long-term maintenance and, of course, the costs.

Civil engineers working for construction contractors are responsible for turning a design into a reality. This involves managing and coordinating the construction workforce, the machinery and materials needed. They deal with any problems that might affect the schedule, the quality of the work and safety of the site workers.

Civil engineering is a wide field, and engineers may choose to specialise in one area, such as:

- structural engineering - working on the design and construction and of all sorts of buildings and structures such as bridges or tall office blocks

- geotechnical engineering - investigating what is underneath the ground's surface

- railway engineering - building overland and underground railways and tramways.

Civil engineers are mainly employed by firms of consulting civil engineers, building and civil engineering contractors, local authorities, government departments and water companies.

Clinical engineer

Clinical engineers (also called biomedical engineers, biomechanical engineers or bioengineers) work on the design, testing and construction of complex machinery and tools that are used in the diagnosis and treatment of medical conditions. Such machines include electronic monitors, scanners, anaesthetic equipment, machines that can take over organ functioning, surgical instruments, laboratory equipment that can test blood, and so on. Clinical engineers also develop artificial joints and limbs, replacement vessels and valves, implants and heart pacemakers. Tissue engineering and robotics are expanding fields of research.

Clinical engineers often work closely with other professionals, such as doctors, physiologists, other engineers, biotechnologists, physicists and computer scientists. Clinical engineers may also work with patients. Rehabilitation engineers, for example, work with patients with disabilities and are involved in the design of custom-made devices that aim to improve patients' quality of life.

The research and development of equipment is carried out in hospitals, research establishments, university engineering and medicine departments, and in medical equipment manufacturing firms.

Computer engineer

Computer engineers are involved in the research, design, development and manufacture of information systems.

An engineer is likely to work on one specific area of an information system. For example:

- **hardware engineers** are involved in developing and building new hardware – such as keyboards, computer processing units, printers, modems, display screens and so on, and of computerised systems used in various other appliances. They may specialise in particular aspects of the work, such as control systems. Hardware engineers have to build prototypes and test them thoroughly before developing them into saleable products.

- **network engineers** develop and install network infrastructures for an organisation. The scale of networks vary widely, from local area networks linking computers within one building, for example, through to worldwide networks, which link systems internationally. Their responsibilities include setting up, managing, trouble-shooting and developing more sophisticated networks, as the organisational requirements change.

Computer engineers often work in teams that include software engineers, systems designers and materials scientists. Hardware engineers are mainly employed by manufacturers of computers, and telecommunications and electronic equipment manufacturers. Network engineers may be employed within an organisation to take responsibility for that organisation's network, or may work for a IT consultancy, working for various clients.

Design engineer

Design engineers, sometimes known as engineering designers, are the creative people at the forefront of all branches of engineering. They are responsible for the technical design of most consumer products, as well as the equipment and machinery used by industry. They may work in areas such as transport, broadcasting systems, medical equipment, aerospace technology, sports equipment and so on! Design engineers work in teams to ensure that they incorporate safety, economy and efficiency into their designs – in order to create products that will perform well, at the right price.

Design engineering is both a technical and creative activity. It involves generating new ideas, evaluating different solutions, producing drawings and specifications, and assessing the financial and commercial aspects of new designs. Computer-aided design (CAD) software is used to model three-dimensional drawings and assess the design's physical properties, such as its flexibility, heat resistance, strength etc. Design engineers may be employed directly by manufacturers or for consultancies that provide design services to industry.

Electrical engineer

Electrical engineers research, develop, install and operate all types of electrical machinery and equipment. There are opportunities to work for:

- energy generation and distribution companies
- manufacturers of all types of electrical equipment
- many types of organisations that use complex electrical equipment, such as factories and mines
- transport companies operating and maintaining trains, ships and aircraft
- in universities and research institutes developing defence and communications systems, for example
- construction firms, developing and installing electrical systems such as power supplies, air conditioning and lifts in new buildings
- the Armed Forces.

Working in research and development may involve producing drawings, testing components and developing prototypes. Electrical engineers working in production management may plan and oversee manufacturing operations, while quality assurance specialists check and test raw materials and finished products. Other opportunities for electrical engineers include working as technical writers, producing detailed instruction manuals, or working in sales and after-sales services, where a high level of technical knowledge is required.

Electronics engineer

Electronics engineers use silicon chip technology to design, manufacture and operate a huge range of items from computers and mobile phones to medical and broadcasting equipment. Engineers also use electronic technology to develop the control systems that operate all sorts of equipment – from satellite tracking systems to washing machines.

Electronics is a rapidly developing field, offering increasing opportunities in areas such as:

- telecommunications – from mobile phone technology to digital communications using fibre optics etc

- nanotechnology – technology that is based on an atomic or molecular scale and has potential applications in computer processors, energy production and so on

- mechatronics – using electronics to drive and control mechanical systems, such as production line robots

- artificial intelligence and cybernetics – systems that sense, measure and respond to variable situations, and through a process of trial and error, can learn to behave in more effective ways.

Mechanical engineer

Mechanical engineers work in a wide range of industries, such as the construction, transport, aerospace, manufacturing, energy and medical industries – or any other industry where mechanical machinery, components or systems are used. As with other fields of engineering, the work may involve designing and testing equipment, building prototypes, servicing and fixing machinery, and providing technical information by means of instruction manuals or after-sales services.

Design projects usually see mechanical engineers working in teams alongside engineers from other disciplines, such as electrical and electronics engineers, on projects to do with renewable energy, for example; or civil engineers on the construction of industrial plants, flood defences and so on. Mechanical engineers may be office-based, but the work can involve visits to outdoor sites or factory production lines.

Production engineer

Production engineers apply their skills of both management and engineering in order to find the most efficient and cost-effective way of converting raw materials into finished products. Working from the prototype of a new product, they must develop the best methods and techniques to bring the item into full production, to the right standards and within budget. They may also be known as manufacturing engineers, plant engineers or operations engineers.

Production engineers may be required to:

- calculate and monitor the efficiency of a production process

- plan, install and commission new production lines, and maintain existing ones
- try to improve the reliability and efficiency of a production process
- find solutions to problems as they arise during production.

The work is technical, but there are also managerial aspects. Production engineers deal not only with the machinery, but also with the people operating it. They often work in teams with technicians (who are responsible for quality and who may supervise craftspeople and operatives), design engineers and purchasing managers (who are responsible for buying in all the necessary raw materials).

Entry qualifications

Most engineers start by taking a relevant higher education qualification. You can take a degree in one of the fields of engineering described above, such as chemical, civil or electronics engineering. Alternatively, you can take a broad-based engineering degree, perhaps specialising towards the end of the degree.

Many engineers work towards incorporated or chartered status. The educational requirements for incorporated engineers are **either** a three-year, full-time (four-year, sandwich) accredited engineering or technology degree course **or** an accredited HNC/D or foundation degree course, plus a further period of learning, to bridge the educational gap to degree level. Prospective chartered engineers must hold **either** an accredited MEng degree course in engineering or technology **or** an accredited BEng degree followed by an accredited masters degree or further learning. To search for accredited courses, visit www.engc.org.uk.

Whatever branch of engineering you are considering, you need to be keen to understand how things work, good at problem solving, ICT and communication skills, and the ability to work well both in a team and independently. Higher-level positions call for management and leadership skills.

Normal colour vision may be necessary for some jobs.

Training and career development

Training may be through a company's graduate training programme, combining experience in the workplace with off-the-job training.

To become registered as either an incorporated engineer or chartered engineer, you must gain the required educational qualifications (see above), become a member of an appropriate institution and then undertake a period of on-the-job training (often called initial professional development), and your competence will be assessed at a professional review.

Chartered engineers have the most creative and innovative jobs. They work at the highest level of research and development, planning, designing and managing major engineering projects. For further information about professional registration, contact the Engineering Council, or view their website.

Those wishing to continue to postgraduate level may consider undertaking an EngD – an alternative to a PhD. Students spend three-quarters of their time working on a project (or projects) with a company, and the rest of the time being taught. Further details can be found on the Engineering and Physical Sciences Research Council's website at www.epsrc.ac.uk.

As their careers progress, incorporated and chartered engineers will find themselves more involved in project management and leading teams of engineers and technicians. To gain promotion, you may have to be prepared to move. Many engineers move into general management. Teaching in further and higher education is also possible. A number of engineers spend at least some of their career working overseas.

Finding vacancies

Employers may advertise their vacancies on their own websites, through specialist recruitment agencies, via online job sites or in the appointment sections of scientific journals. Many professional bodies advertise opportunities on their websites.

While at university, or as a recent graduate, you can access information about potential employers and current graduate vacancies through your university careers service. Further information about the help available through university careers services is provided in Chapter three.

Sources of further information

The Chartered Institution of Building Services Engineers (CIBSE) – tel: 020 8675 5211. www.cibse.org

Energy & Utility Skills – the Sector Skills Council for the gas, power, waste management and water industries. Tel: 0845 077 9922. www.euskills.co.uk

Engineering Council – tel: 020 3206 0500. www.engc.org.uk

EngineeringUK – tel: 020 3206 0400. www.engineeringuk.com

IET (The Institution of Engineering and Technology) – tel: 01438 313311. www.theiet.org

Institute of Physics and Engineering in Medicine – tel: 01904 610821. www.ipem.ac.uk

Institution of Chemical Engineers – tel: 01788 578214. www.icheme.org
For information on courses, careers and jobs, see www.whynotchemeng.com

Institution of Civil Engineers (ICE) – tel: 020 7222 7722. www.ice.org.uk/education

The Institution of Engineering Designers – tel: 01373 822801. www.ied.org.uk

Institution of Lighting Engineers – tel: 01788 576492. www.ile.org.uk

Institution of Mechanical Engineers (IMechE) – tel: 020 7222 7899. www.imeche.org

The Institution of Structural Engineers – tel: 020 7235 4535. www.istructe.org

Royal Aeronautical Society – tel: 020 7670 4300. www.raes.org.uk

Semta – the Sector Skills Council for science, engineering and manufacturing technologies. Tel: 0800 282 167 (learning helpline). www.semta.org.uk

SOE (Society of Operations Engineers) – tel: 020 7630 1111. www.soe.org.uk

WISE (Women Into Science, Engineering and Construction) – tel: 020 3206 0408. www.wisecampaign.org.uk

Women's Engineering Society – tel: 01438 765506. www.wes.org.uk

www.enginuity.org.uk – provides careers information.

www.scenta.co.uk – provides careers information.

Section 3

Other careers you could consider

Chapter nine

Careers in communication and media

This chapter outlines some of the jobs available in:

- advertising
- public relations (PR)
- journalism.

These career areas are often perceived to be quite glamorous and exciting, so employers are normally spoilt for choice when looking for new employees! While you may be competing for jobs with non-graduates, having a degree is a definite advantage. Your degree can usually be in any subject, although taking a pre-entry course relevant to the area of work you want to enter may be preferred, or possibly even essential. Having a degree in an unrelated field, such as science, may help you find specialist work, for example writing for a scientific journal, or providing PR services to a scientific company.

Advertising and public relations

Advertising

Advertising involves promoting products and services to a target market, such as consumers or other businesses. It requires creativity but also a good understanding of the needs of the customer and the most appropriate way to communicate with them.

While in-house jobs are available, most of the work in advertising is carried out through advertising agencies working on behalf of other organisations. Typical agency roles for graduates include: account executive, account planner, copywriter and media executive.

Account executives act as the intermediary between the agency and the client organisation. They receive a brief from the client and plan a marketing strategy and advertising campaign to meet their needs. The account executive may lead a team of colleagues who 'pitch' the campaign idea to the client, and if successful in gaining their business, oversees the implementation of the campaign.

Account planners research and analyse the market in order to advise on the most appropriate audience to target and how best to reach them. They help develop the advertising campaign and monitor the competition.

Adverts appear in many forms and media - television, radio, newspapers, posters, emails and on the internet, for example. **Copywriters** are responsible for any text that is used in an advert. Copywriting requires creativity, excellent communication skills and the ability to be concise and persuasive, while meeting the client's brief.

The effectiveness and cost of a campaign is directly related to the media that are used to carry the advertising. **Media planners** analyse market research data to identify and recommend the most appropriate media to reach the target audience. **Media buyers** negotiate with media owners, such as owners of poster sites or companies that run television or radio stations, to buy the advertising space or time.

Public relations

Public relations (PR) work covers all the aspects of establishing good relations between an organisation and its public - whether customers, shareholders, the local community or general public. Creating, and keeping up, a positive image and reputation is a delicate business, requiring careful forward planning and ongoing effort. The work can involve:

- media relations – presenting your organisation to the press, TV, radio etc

- organising corporate hospitality events

- public affairs – presenting your organisation's ideas to those in government

- managing the reputation of your organisation

- financial relations – a specialist area concerned with attracting investors.

As a **PR officer** you may conduct research before planning, delivering and evaluating a programme of activities. You may organise events such as conferences, exhibitions and open days to promote the organisation. Ongoing work may involve maintaining good relations with the media – writing and editing press releases, handling enquiries from journalists, and organising interviews and press conferences – although this is often a specialist role undertaken by a **press officer**.

Entry qualifications

Advertising and PR are very popular career areas and entry is fiercely competitive. You may be competing with people who have degrees in subjects more relevant to this type of work. However jobs are usually available to graduates of any subject and employers may be more concerned about the personal qualities and interests of potential employees. Work experience and postgraduate qualifications in a relevant subject may be useful.

Clearly, excellent communication skills are required, in terms of dealing with colleagues and clients, and also in relation to creating the finished product, be it an advert or press release. Many roles in this field require creativity and the ability to work on several projects at once. Self-confidence is important and the work often relies on building and maintaining a good network of contacts. You may be expected to work long, irregular hours to meet deadlines.

Training and career development

Once in employment, it may be possible to take a professional qualification, such as those offered by The CAM Foundation, the Chartered Institute of Marketing or the Chartered Institute of Public Relations. Agencies that are members of the Institute of Practitioners in Advertising offer their graduates an induction programme and access to a training scheme for career development.

Finding vacancies

Vacancies are advertised on the websites of some of the relevant professional bodies, by specialist recruitment agencies, on many specialist and general online job sites, in the appointments sections of certain daily newspapers and on employers' own websites.

While at university, or as a recent graduate, you can access information about potential employers and current graduate vacancies through your university careers service. Further information about the help available through university careers services is provided in Chapter three

Sources of further information

Advertising Association – tel: 020 7340 1100. www.adassoc.org.uk

CAM (Communication, Advertising and Marketing) Foundation – tel: 01628 427120. www.camfoundation.com

The Chartered Institute of Marketing (CIM) – tel: 01628 427120. www.cim.co.uk

Chartered Institute of Public Relations (CIPR) – tel: 020 7631 6900. www.cipr.co.uk

The Institute of Direct Marketing (IDM) – tel: 020 8977 5705. www.theidm.com

Institute of Practitioners in Advertising (IPA) – tel: 020 7235 7020. www.ipa.co.uk

Internet Advertising Bureau – tel: 020 7050 6969. www.iabuk.net

Public Relations Consultants Association – tel: 020 7233 6026. www.prca.org.uk

Skillset – the Sector Skills Council covering the advertising industry. Helpline: 08080 300 900 (in England and N.Ireland) or 0800 012 1815 (in Wales). www.skillset.org/careers

Journalism

Journalists research information for reports and articles by various means – through face-to-face, telephone or email interviews, by going to meetings and press conferences, by following up leads from the public, by contact with the emergency services etc. They may then write up the story, ready for printing in a newspaper or magazine, or publishing on a website, or tell the story through the broadcast media. Journalists are sometimes required to take photographs or record/edit audio and video to go with their articles and scripts.

Journalists can work for local, regional and national newspapers, news agencies, press offices of large companies and government organisations, the vast range of weekly and monthly periodicals, radio and TV broadcasting companies and, increasingly, multimedia companies and internet news services.

Entry qualifications

Most people prepare for a career in journalism by taking a pre-entry training course in journalism accredited by either the National Council for the Training of Journalists (NCTJ), the Periodicals Training Council (PTC) or the Broadcast Journalism Training Council (BJTC). Many of these courses lead to postgraduate qualifications, although not all. While a degree is required for some pre-entry courses, some will accept applicants with lower-level qualifications. As a minimum, you will need two A levels or equivalent qualifications, plus five supporting GCSEs, including English at grades A*-C. Most colleges expect applicants for pre-entry courses to have undertaken relevant work experience.

Some employers may offer direct entry onto their own training schemes, although you are likely to need a good portfolio of work (such as published articles from a student newspaper) and a degree in a subject that indicates you have specialist knowledge relevant to the role.

On a personal level, you will need to be able to demonstrate an interest in news and current affairs and be prepared to work long hours, often under pressure, in order to meet strict deadlines. You will need determination, drive and persistence as well as excellent people-skills. Journalists also need to be able to write accurately, succinctly and engagingly. Shorthand, keyboarding and general IT skills are important.

Training and career development

Once employed, training is mainly on the job. It may be possible to attend short courses accredited by the NCTJ, PTC or BJTC.

The way in which news is delivered is changing, for example via mobile phones and other digital technologies, so journalists need new and different skills. Many employers now expect journalists to develop cross-media skills - to be able to research a story and then present it in different styles for print, broadcast and online versions, as well as perhaps maintain blogs and add other content to websites.

With experience, it may be possible to work as a freelance journalist. Opportunities for progression vary depending on the media. In newspaper and magazine journalism, it may be possible to take on responsibility for a whole section, before promotion to sub-editor, deputy editor, then editor of an entire publication. Broadcast journalists, who may start out as researchers or newsroom assistants, may be promoted to on-air roles such as reporters or presenters, or move into production or management.

Finding vacancies

Vacancies are often advertised on employers' own websites - links to some of the main employers can be found on the websites of the Newspaper Society, the Periodical Publishers Association (PPA) and the BJTC.

Alternatively, search for vacancies through specialist recruitment agencies, specialist and general online job sites, and in the appointments sections of certain daily newspapers (particularly the media section of The Guardian, published every Monday).

While at university, or as a recent graduate, you can access information about potential employers and current graduate vacancies through your university careers service. Further information about the help available through university careers services is provided in Chapter three

Sources of further information

Broadcast Journalism Training Council - tel: 01778 440025.
www.bjtc.org.uk

Chartered Institute of Journalists - tel: 020 7252 1187.
www.cioj.co.uk

National Council for the Training of Journalists (NCTJ) – tel: 01799 544014. www.nctj.com

National Union of Journalists – tel: 020 7278 7916. www.nuj.org.uk and www.nujtraining.org.uk

Newspaper Society – tel: 020 7632 7400. www.newspapersoc.org.uk

Periodical Publishers Association – tel: 020 7404 4166. www.ppa.co.uk

Periodicals Training Council – tel: 020 7400 7533. www.ppa.co.uk

Skillset – the Sector Skills Council for creative media. Helpline: 08080 300 900 (in England and N.Ireland) or 0800 012 1815 (in Wales). www.skillset.org/careers

Chapter ten

Careers in education

This chapter covers teaching:

- in state schools
- in further education
- in higher education
- English to speakers of other languages.

Although teaching can be challenging, the emotional rewards can be huge. It takes imagination, confidence and communication skills to help others achieve their potential. In general, teachers specialise in teaching subjects closely linked to the subject of their degree. However, it is also possible to train to teach other, unrelated, subjects, depending on the type of work you go into.

Teachers have many duties alongside taking lessons, such as planning, preparation and assessment. In order to ensure students are supported effectively, teachers attend meetings and liaise with other interested parties, such as teaching colleagues, other professionals and parents. There is also a considerable amount of record keeping required of each student's learning and progress. New initiatives and developments in particular subjects mean that teachers must undergo continuous professional development (CPD) to keep up to date.

Teaching in state schools

Primary teachers work with pupils from the age of four or five up to eleven. They teach the subjects that are set out in the National Curriculum, but focus a great deal on developing pupils' literacy (reading, writing, listening and speaking) and numeracy (number skills, mental arithmetic and so on). Teaching at primary level requires a great deal of enthusiasm and creativity, and the ability to adapt your teaching style to varying ability levels. Teachers often take on a carer's role, tending minor ills and sorting out children's problems.

Secondary teachers are usually specialists in one or two subjects from the National Curriculum. Schools may also offer subjects outside of the National Curriculum as GCSE, AS/A level or Diploma options, such as leisure and tourism, engineering, manufacturing and product design. Secondary teachers may be required to take on a tutorial role and be involved in the delivery of personal, social, health and economic education (PSHE).

Financial incentives are available to those training to teach those subjects where there are teacher shortages. In recent times, there has been a shortage of teachers in maths, physics, chemistry and modern languages.

Entry qualifications

Your degree needs to be in a subject relevant to the National Curriculum. You also need GCSEs in English and maths at grades A*-C (or equivalent qualifications). If you wish to train as a primary teacher, you also need a GCSE in science at grade A*-C (or equivalent).

An empathy with children and a patient, tolerant and sensitive approach are obviously important personal qualities required by teachers. Good communication and listening skills, and a sound knowledge of your subject(s) are essential. For primary teaching, in particular, a wide range of abilities and interests may be beneficial, such as in arts and crafts, sport, music or drama.

If you are considering a career in teaching, it is essential that you gain classroom experience before applying for training, so that you can show an understanding of the teacher's role. Contact the Training and Development Agency for Schools (TDA) for advice about how you can gain relevant work experience.

Before starting your training, you will need to undergo checks on your suitability to teach (including criminal record, background, health, identity and employment checks).

Training and career development

To teach in a state school, you need to follow initial teacher training (ITT) leading to Qualified Teacher Status (QTS). After which you must complete an induction period and then register with the appropriate General Teaching Council (GTC) depending on which part of the country you work in. During your training, you specialise in teaching pupils of a particular age range.

Graduates can train to become teachers by taking a postgraduate course (PGCE) or an employment-based route, as described below.

Universities and colleges offer one-year, full-time courses leading to a **PGCE** (which stands for both the Postgraduate Certificate in Education and the Professional Graduate Certificate in Education). The Professional Certificate is at honours-degree level, while the Postgraduate Certificate is academically more demanding. Both types of PGCE aim to develop your teaching skills by combining classroom practice with academic study. There are also some part-time, flexible- and distance-learning routes.

Alternatively, training for a PGCE may be through a group of schools that offers SCITT (School-Centred Initial Teacher Training). This involves more time in the classroom and is usually taught by practising teachers.

There are special courses for people who need to boost their subject knowledge – particularly in shortage subjects. Contact the TDA for further details.

Employment-based training routes include the Graduate Teacher Programme (GTP), and Teach First. These offer graduates the chance to work, and earn a salary, as unqualified teachers, while receiving much of their training in school.

Qualified teachers can look to develop their careers in a number of ways. Staying within the classroom, it may be possible to train as a special educational needs (SEN) teacher or as an advanced skills teacher. There are opportunities to move into school management, ultimately to the level of headteacher. Experienced teachers can also consider roles in the wider educational field, such as a teacher trainer; Ofsted inspector; education officer for a museum, zoo, etc; adviser for a local authority education department, exam board or educational charity; and so on.

Finding vacancies

Applications for PGCEs are usually made through the Graduate Teacher Training Registry (GTTR). Alternatively, some SCITT providers accept direct applications. The TDA website has further information.

To apply for the GTP you usually need to find a school willing to employ you before applying to your local GTP training provider. You can search for details of employing schools and training providers in your area via the TDA website. Teach First operates an online recruitment system via a dedicated website (see below).

General teaching vacancies may be advertised by local authorities via their regular bulletins or on their websites, on the official recruitment website for local government jobs (www.LGjobs.com), on schools' own websites, or every Friday in the *Times Educational Supplement*.

While at university, or as a recent graduate, you can access information about potential employers and current graduate vacancies through your university careers service. Further information about the help available through university careers services is provided in Chapter three.

Sources of further information

General Teaching Council for England – tel: 0870 001 0308. www.gtce.org.uk

General Teaching Council for Wales – tel: 029 2055 0350. www.gtcw.org.uk

Graduate Teacher Training Registry (GTTR) – tel: 0871 468 0469. www.gttr.ac.uk

Teach First – tel: 0844 880 1800. www.teachfirst.org.uk

Teacher Training & Education in Wales – www.teachertrainingwales.org

Training and Development Agency for Schools (TDA) – tel: 0845 6000 991 (or 0845 6000 922 for Welsh speakers). www.tda.gov.uk

Teaching in further education

The majority of further education (FE) takes place in FE and sixth-form colleges and is aimed at students aged between 16 and 19. However, FE may also refer to education provided in adult and community learning, work-based learning and offender-learning settings.

Teachers in FE deliver a huge variety of subjects and qualifications, such as:

- work-related courses in subjects such as horticulture and engineering

- GCSEs and A levels
- Access courses for people who want to go on to higher education (HE)
- some HE courses – foundation degrees, HNCs, HNDs and degrees
- courses leading to qualifications from professional bodies.

Alongside all the typical work of a teacher, FE teachers are likely to be involved in recruiting and selecting students for their courses, acting as a personal tutor and fostering strong links with local employers. The work may involve teaching evening classes and classes during college holidays.

There are two teaching roles within FE: **full teacher** (has the full range of teaching responsibilities, including developing the curriculum and planning how it will be taught) and **associate teacher** (has fewer responsibilities; for example, may teach from a pre-prepared pack). To work in either role, you need a qualification endorsed by Standards Verification UK (SVUK).

Entry qualifications

Depending on the courses you intend to teach, you will need professional or academic qualifications in those areas, and relevant business/industrial experience for work-related subjects. With a degree, it is possible to teach academic subjects at least up to A level.

Obviously, a thorough and up-to-date knowledge of your subject is essential for this type of work; you will also need strong communication and organisation skills, flexibility and enthusiasm for teaching people from a wide range of backgrounds.

You need to undergo background checks if you intend to work with children, young people or vulnerable adults.

Training and career development

To qualify as an associate teacher, you need to complete the Certificate in Teaching in the Lifelong Learning Sector (CTLLS). Courses leading to the CTLLS are usually offered on a part-time basis, and are aimed at those already employed in the FE sector. Following this, you need to complete a period of assessed work experience known as professional formation. On completion, you can apply for Associate Teacher Learning and Skills (ATLS) status.

Full teachers have the option of completing either of the following:

- the Diploma in Teaching in the Lifelong Learning Sector (DTLLS)
- the Postgraduate Certificate in Education (PGCE) Post-Compulsory Education and Training (PCET).

These qualifications can either be taken prior to employment in the sector as a one-year, full-time course, or if you already have a teaching post, as a two-year, part-time course.

Following this, you need to complete your professional formation. On completion, you can apply for Qualified Teacher Learning and Skills (QTLS) status.

FE teachers need to be registered with the Institute for Learning (IfL).

N.B. In Wales, there is currently no equivalent requirement to ATLS/QTLS, but there may be in the future. To teach in an FE college in Wales, you need to have or gain a teaching qualification that is endorsed by SVUK. For more information, contact Lifelong Learning UK (LLUK) - the Sector Skills Council covering FE education.

Finding vacancies

Vacancies are advertised on the Association of Colleges' website, and on websites of individual colleges. Vacancies are also listed every Friday in the *Times Educational Supplement*.

While at university, or as a recent graduate, you can access information about potential employers and current graduate vacancies through your university careers service. Further information about the help available through university careers services is provided in Chapter three.

Sources of further information

Association of Colleges - tel: 020 7299 6980. www.aoc.co.uk

Institute for Learning (IfL) - tel: 0844 815 3202. www.ifl.ac.uk

Lifelong Learning UK (LLUK) - tel: 0300 303 1877. www.lluk.org

Standards Verification UK (SVUK) - tel: 0113 241 0427. www.standardsverificationuk.org

Teaching in higher education

Teaching in higher education (HE) is often combined with research. This research may be purely academic, or it may be sponsored by industry to solve practical problems. Teaching can involve one-to-one tutorials, group seminars of, say, 10 to 20 students, or lectures that may be given to groups of anything from 25 to a few hundred students. 'Virtual' lectures are sometimes given via the internet.

Subjects taught at HE level include traditional academic subjects, such as physics or history, as well as work-related subjects, such as architecture or physiotherapy. HE institutions may also offer courses leading to professional qualifications. Subjects are also taught at postgraduate level.

Entry qualifications

You will be teaching very able students who already have level 3 qualifications (A levels, Advanced Diplomas, etc), so you need to be highly qualified in your subject area – typically with a good honours degree, plus a masters degree or, preferably, a PhD.

Training and career development

Many lecturers start out as postgraduate research assistants or teaching assistants, being paid to assist while gaining their own postgraduate qualifications. This can often lead to a lecturer's post, once qualified.

Increasingly, HE institutions expect their teaching staff to undergo some formal teacher training or, at least, in-house induction and professional development programmes. This may involve a probationary period and mentoring. The quality of teaching is one of the factors looked at when HE courses and institutions are inspected.

The Higher Education Academy operates a professional recognition scheme. Experienced teaching staff, and those who have completed professional development schemes that are recognised by the academy, can achieve associate, fellow or senior fellow status. For more information, see the academy website, listed below.

University and college lecturers can be promoted to senior or principal lecturer posts, or professorships. The highest post is vice-chancellor of a university. Many academics also publish books or write articles for journals on their subject. Some, who are particularly good communicators, present radio and television programmes.

Finding vacancies

Jobs are advertised in the *THE* (*Times Higher Education*) every Friday, as well as in certain newspapers, and on the websites of individual HE institutions.

While at university, or as a recent graduate, you can access information about potential employers and current graduate vacancies through your university careers service. Further information about the help available through university careers services is provided in Chapter three.

Sources of further information

The Higher Education Academy – tel: 01904 717500.
www.heacademy.ac.uk

Teaching English to speakers of other languages

There are opportunities to work in the UK and abroad teaching English to speakers of other languages, generally referred to as TESOL. In the UK, you can teach English in a commercial language school, FE college, community and adult learning setting, or HE institution. Or you may be employed to provide English language support to foreign students while they are studying in the UK. Overseas, there are opportunities to teach English with commercial language schools, voluntary organisations, large employers and the British Council.

Whatever the setting, what you teach will depend on the needs of your students. They may want to be able to read, write and speak English to a high level, perhaps for business purposes. Some may just want to speak and understand the language at a basic level. In some situations, you may have contact with your students over a long period; in others, you may be teaching students on short, intensive courses. Classes are usually small, and may involve teaching on a one-to-one basis.

Entry qualifications

Recognised UK-based language schools expect teachers to be graduates and to hold a relevant English language teaching qualification. Requirements to teach overseas vary; however, most reputable employers require the same standards as UK-based language schools.

In order to teach in the FE sector in England, teachers need to have Qualified Teacher Learning and Skills (QTLS) status and be registered with the Institute for Learning. They also need a specific qualification for TESOL, which can be taken separately or as part of the DTLLS (see earlier).

N.B. These regulations do not apply to teachers in further education in Wales, where there are currently no specific minimum qualifications to teach ESOL. Employers set their own entry requirements. However, this is under review and is likely to change. For up-to-date information contact Lifelong Learning UK.

The British Council only employs graduates who have an acceptable teaching qualification and a minimum of two years' relevant experience.

Training and career development

There are a number of courses available, ranging from introductory or taster courses through to advanced-level qualifications, offered by different examining bodies at accredited centres and via distance learning. The two main organisations that award relevant qualifications are the University of Cambridge ESOL Examinations and Trinity College London.

Various postgraduate courses offered by universities and other HE institutions provide specialist study in, or relevant to, TESOL. These vary so much that the syllabus of each should be examined carefully to see whether the content is really relevant to your particular requirements.

Although opportunities for promotion are limited in this line of work, there may be opportunities to move into a managerial position in a large school or college. You could also think about specialising, for example in teaching business English. Self-employment is an option – you could set up your own language school or undertake private tuition.

Finding vacancies

Vacancies are advertised on the online version of *EL Gazette*, as well as on many general online job sites.

While at university, or as a recent graduate, you can access information about potential employers and current graduate vacancies through your university careers service. Further information about the help available through university careers services is provided in Chapter three.

Sources of further information

British Council Information Centre – tel: 0161 957 7755. www.britishcouncil.org/teacherrecruitment

English UK – association of over 400 providers of English language teaching in Britain that are accredited by the British Council. Tel: 020 7608 7960. www.englishuk.com

International House London – a major employer of teachers in its language schools overseas, and a teacher training provider. Tel: 020 7611 2400. www.ihlondon.com

Trinity College London – tel: 020 7820 6100. www.trinitycollege.co.uk

University of Cambridge ESOL Examinations – www.cambridgeesol.org

Chapter eleven

Careers in finance

Opportunities for financial specialists are not just limited to the financial services sector; all areas of the economy require people who can manage money, including the public sector, industry and commerce, and individuals. As a graduate you could consider working:

- as an accountant
- as an actuary
- in a bank or building society
- in insurance
- as a stockbroker.

Accountant

There are three main areas in which accountants work. Most accountants work in **private practice** (sometimes confusingly referred to as public practice), which means they are employed by an accountancy firm to provide financial services to individuals and to organisations of all types and sizes. Accountants working in **industry and commerce** offer in-house expertise for their employer's business. **Public sector** accountants work for local government, the NHS and other public services where the emphasis is on ensuring taxpayers' money is spent as efficiently as possible. The exact nature of the work varies according to your specialism.

Financial accountants oversee the financial transactions of an organisation. This entails managing the payment of wages, taxes, invoices and so on; ensuring details of all income and expenditure are recorded; preparing the accounts and reports for directors; managing investments and protecting assets; and carrying out internal audits of the organisation's financial affairs.

Management accountants collect and analyse an organisation's financial information in order to forecast results, create business plans, control budgets, perform cost/benefit analysis of future projects and prepare management reports. In effect, they act as internal consultants specialising in the financial performance of the organisation.

Auditors examine accounts that others have prepared to check that they are a 'true and fair view' of the organisation's affairs. This involves interviewing staff at all levels and checking supporting documents to find out how the data was compiled, what policies are in place and how they are enforced. Internal auditors look at the accounts of the organisation they work for and offer advice on best practice. External auditors can either work for private firms that audit company accounts for clients, or public sector organisations such as the Audit Commission or the National Audit Office, which seek to ensure that local and central government, the NHS, etc provide good value for money.

Accountants can specialise in many other areas relating to finance. For example, **taxation specialists** provide advice to individuals and organisations about their tax status and liabilities and negotiate tax assessments with HM Revenue & Customs (HMRC). **Insolvency specialists** work with failing businesses to guide them through the winding-up process – selling off assets and paying creditors. **Corporate finance specialists** support companies involved in mergers and acquisitions, by producing business plans and financial projections, as well as advising on methods of raising the necessary finance.

Entry qualifications

Training leading to chartered status is through one of the professional accountancy bodies, which include:

- the Institute of Chartered Accountants in England and Wales (ICAEW)
- the Association of Chartered Certified Accountants (ACCA)
- the Chartered Institute of Management Accountants (CIMA)
- the Chartered Institute of Public Finance and Accountancy (CIPFA).

To qualify you need to pass professional exams and undertake a period of practical experience. Although a degree is not required by the accountancy bodies to begin training, in practice, many accountants are graduates and employers offering training contracts may require at least a 2:1 degree for entry. In addition, you are normally expected to have a strong academic track record at GCSE and A level (or equivalent).

As you would expect, accountants need a good level of numeracy, ICT skills and the ability to analyse information, but must also be able to communicate complex ideas to non-specialists and have a logical mind and an interest in business.

Training and career development

The professional accountancy bodies offer several routes to qualifying, including training on the job, part- or full-time college courses, and distance learning. Training can take from between three to four years, including relevant work experience. Note that qualifying as a chartered accountant involves a level of study equivalent to taking another degree, usually while doing a full-time job! All accountants are expected to take part in continuing professional development (CPD) throughout their careers.

Training for an accountancy qualification is excellent preparation for a general management career in almost any area of the economy. For example, while it is not a prerequisite, many company directors, chief executives and company secretaries first trained as accountants. In the public sector, accountants can progress to the level of chief financial officer or treasurer of a local authority, for example. In private practice, it is possible to become a partner of a firm of accountants or be self-employed. Accountancy training can also be good preparation for someone who wants to start to run any other type of enterprise, because it can develop both business awareness and knowledge of financial management.

Finding vacancies

Vacancies are advertised on the websites of the professional accountancy bodies, by specialist recruitment agencies, on many specialist and general online job sites, in publications such as *Accountancy* and *Accountancy Age*, in the appointments sections of certain daily newspapers and on employers' own websites.

While at university, or as a recent graduate, you can access information about potential employers and current graduate vacancies through your university careers service. Further information about the help available through university careers services is provided in Chapter three.

Sources of further information

Association of Chartered Certified Accountants (ACCA) – tel: 020 7059 5000. www.accaglobal.com

Association of International Accountants (AIA) – tel: 0191 493 0277. www.aiaworldwide.com

Audit Commission – tel: 0844 798 1212. www.everybody-counts.co.uk and www.whatisyouraudit.com

Chartered Institute of Management Accountants (CIMA) – tel: 020 8849 2251. www.cimaglobal.com

Chartered Institute of Public Finance & Accountancy (CIPFA) – tel: 020 7543 5600. www.cipfa.org.uk

Institute of Chartered Accountants in England and Wales (ICAEW) – tel: 01908 248040. www.icaew.com

Institute of Financial Accountants (IFA) – tel: 01732 458080. www.ifa.org.uk

National Audit Office – tel: 020 7798 7227. www.nao.org.uk

Actuary

Actuaries calculate risks – the probability of certain things happening – and then apply their findings to financial problems, such as how much people should pay for life insurance or into their pensions. Statistics and probability theory are the basis of much of their work.

Actuaries are employed in many areas of the financial sector, including insurance, investment, pensions and specialist consultancy. Some work in the public sector for the Government Actuary's Department (GAD), which advises the UK government, and other countries, on pensions policy and regulation, social security benefits, occupational pensions, insurance and so on.

Entry qualifications

Most entrants to the profession have a degree in a numerate subject, such as maths, statistics, engineering or physics, although it is possible for graduates who have a first- or second-class degree in any subject to go into actuarial work provided they can demonstrate a high-level of numeracy, such as through an A level in maths at grade A*-C. The Actuarial Profession (an organisation that represents the professional actuarial bodies covering England, Wales and Scotland) offers a Certificate in financial mathematics, suitable for undergraduates who want to enhance their career prospects in the finance sector.

While mathematical ability is clearly required, actuaries must also be able to communicate clearly to non-specialists, both orally and in writing.

Training and career development

To qualify as an actuary in England and Wales, you must pass the professional exams of the Institute of Actuaries while working in a suitable training position. It can take between three and six years to qualify. Tuition for the exams is by the Actuarial Education Company and usually combines distance learning and personal tuition. Your path is made easier if you undertake a postgraduate course in actuarial science as this, as well as relevant degrees, can earn exemptions from some of the professional examinations.

Actuaries can move out of specific actuarial work into middle and senior management, especially in life insurance companies and pension funds.

Finding vacancies

Vacancies are advertised in *The Actuary*, published monthly, and on its associated website. A list of actuarial employers can be found on the website of the Actuarial Profession. Vacancies are also advertised by specialist recruitment agencies, on many specialist and general online job sites, and in the appointments sections of certain daily newspapers.

While at university, or as a recent graduate, you can access information about potential employers and current graduate vacancies through your university careers service. Further information about the help that is available through university careers services is provided in Chapter three.

Sources of further information

The Actuarial Profession – incorporates the Institute of Actuaries. Tel: 020 7632 2100. www.actuaries.org.uk

www.the-actuary.org.uk – the online version of *The Actuary*, the monthly magazine for the actuarial profession.

Bank or building society work

Retail banks and building societies provide many of the same financial services – they offer current accounts and savings accounts; lend money and issue credit cards; clear cheques and transfer funds; invest money; buy and sell foreign currency; and sell a range of 'financial products' to individuals and organisations. The main difference between them is that retail banks are owned by shareholders, while building societies are owned by their members – the people who deposit money with them or who take out mortgages from them.

Managers in retail banks and building societies are responsible for the day-to-day running of a branch, a region of branches or a specialist department at headquarters. They must attract business to the organisation by offering financial products and services that customers want, while at the same time managing risk, for example, by assessing the credit-worthiness of individuals or firms. Within a branch, they manage and train the customer services team and spend a lot of time visiting businesses – discussing their business plans, loans, insurance and other needs. Within head office, there are opportunities to specialise in financial legal work (such as compliance), ICT, marketing, insurance, investment management, human resources and training, and financial administration.

Investment banks, also known as corporate or merchant banks, provide services similar to the retail banks but to customers that range from small businesses to multinational corporations and overseas governments. As well as taking deposits, making loans and transferring funds, their work includes financing international trade, advising on mergers and takeovers, and raising capital. They buy and sell foreign currency and manage pension funds and investment trusts. They help companies acquire assets, such as a fleet of new lorries, by buying them and leasing them to the customer. They are also involved in floating companies on the stock market and buying and selling shares.

The Bank of England acts as banker to the Government and to the other banks. It is responsible for issuing and destroying banknotes, setting interest rates, and has responsibilities for other institutions in the money and foreign exchange markets. It has a key role in government financial policies and is vital to the functioning of the economy. Much of its work involves the collection, analysis and interpretation of economic and financial data relating both to the British economy and to economic conditions abroad.

Most retail banks have large **international banking** divisions, with operations in the major financial centres of the world. Similarly, many overseas banks have branches in the UK, particularly London. Staff are usually recruited from the local area and normally only very senior staff get the opportunity to work abroad. International banking careers therefore involve working in this country, but specialising in foreign exchange, shipping documents, foreign stocks and shares etc. As well as the direct banking careers, there are openings in specialist roles such as audit, accountancy, actuarial work and ICT.

Entry qualifications

Management trainee schemes offered by retail banks, building societies and investment banks usually require at least a second-class degree in any subject for entry. The Bank of England requires at least a 2:1, plus a minimum of 300 UCAS Tariff points at A level (or equivalent) for entry onto its graduate scheme, known as the Analyst Career Training (ACT) programme. Because most banks and building societies have large branch networks, you are normally required to be mobile and able to lead a team. Good communication and ICT skills are also essential.

Training and career development

Graduate training schemes combine work experience in a variety of functions with a programme of study. These studies lead to professional qualifications, such as those offered by the *ifs* School of Finance. Progress within the banking sector depends on your performance. You may move up in management roles of increasing seniority or become a specialist in a particular area.

Finding vacancies

Employers advertise details of their graduate training schemes on their own websites. Vacancies are also advertised by specialist recruitment agencies, on many specialist and general online job sites, and in the appointments sections of certain daily newspapers.

While at university, or as a recent graduate, you can access information about potential employers and current graduate vacancies through your university careers service. Further information about the help available through university careers services is provided in Chapter three.

Sources of further information

Bank of England – tel: 020 7601 4444. www.bankofenglandjobs.co.uk

Barclays Bank – tel: 0845 241 4936. www.barclays-graduates.co.uk

Britannia Building Society – www.britannia.co.uk

The Building Societies Association - tel: 020 7520 5900.
www.bsa.org.uk

Financial Services Skills Council - the Sector Skills Council for financial services, accountancy and finance. Tel: 0845 257 3772.
www.fssc.org.uk

HSBC - http://jobs.hsbc.co.uk/graduates

ifs **School of Finance** - tel: 01227 818609. www.ifslearning.ac.uk

Lloyds Banking Group - which includes Lloyds TSB, Halifax and Bank of Scotland. www.lloydsbankinggrouptalent.com

Nationwide - www.nationwide-jobs.co.uk

RBS - The Royal Bank of Scotland Group, which includes NatWest.
www.makeitrbs.com

Santander - www.santanderukgraduates.com

Insurance work

Insurance is a way of protecting people from losses arising from sickness, theft, fire, accident and other misfortunes. Insurance is based on the laws of probability: that is, the likelihood of certain events occurring or happening to people. The principle behind it is that many people regularly pay into a common fund but only a few people will need to claim compensation for a loss.

The insurance sector in the UK comprises:

- several hundred insurance companies - some specialise in particular areas such as vehicle, marine, commercial, health or aviation, while others provide a wide range of services

- insurance brokers - who act as intermediaries between the customer and the insurer to help customers find the best policies, often negotiating on their behalf

- the famous Lloyd's of London - which is an insurance 'market' where the insurance cover, usually for large-scale risks, is provided by syndicates of individuals.

Underwriters, both in the insurance companies and those in Lloyd's, are responsible for calculating the risks, deciding whether they are insurable and, if so, on what terms. Some risks are simple to assess and are based on standard guidelines. Others, such as for the Olympic Games or a space satellite, are more complex and unique. It is here that the specialist skills of an underwriter are required to work out premiums and the terms and conditions of the policy. Technical advice may be provided by insurance surveyors.

Insurance surveyors visit the commercial site or property that is to be insured and report on any aspects that might affect the underwriter's assessment, such as the use of dangerous materials, fire risks and security. Surveyors also advise clients on how to reduce their risks (and so their premiums) through improved security, safer storage of flammable materials and so on. The work may also include carrying out surveys of ships, aircraft, etc. The work of an insurance surveyor can include a large amount of travel, possibly including overseas. Insurance surveyors are often drawn from existing staff and given appropriate training. There is a trend towards employing graduates with a scientific or engineering background.

When claims are made, claims staff assess the loss and decide the amount to be paid. Some claim assessments are quite simple and will be handled by **claims technicians**. Others may require the intervention of **claims negotiators** who have expert knowledge of medicine, the law, or some aspect of science or technology. The claims negotiator may need to visit the site of the claim, interview witnesses and inspect damage before deciding on the outcome of the claim. For large, complex or disputed claims, the insurer may bring in a **loss adjuster** to examine the claim and help to reach a settlement. The insured party may also employ their own independent loss adjuster to negotiate the claim on their behalf.

Insurance agents are authorised by insurance companies to sell a wide range of insurance products on their behalf to the general public and to brokers. **Brokers** are experts in insurance and help their clients to choose and buy the best insurance policy to meet their needs. They earn commission from the insurer once a policy has been bought and may be self-employed or work for large firms of brokers. Brokers must have a wide knowledge of the insurance market, insurance law and practice. Although their main function is to get the best type of cover for their clients, they may also advise on how to lessen risks by improving fire precautions, isolating dangerous materials and so on.

Entry qualifications

Usually, any degree subject is acceptable for entry onto graduate training schemes, although mathematical and business-related disciplines are particularly relevant. You need to be numerate, have an analytical mind and be able to combine assertiveness with tact (you may have to deal sensitively with people who have suffered various calamities). You must be a persuasive communicator, both orally and in writing.

Training and career development

Your training is likely to combine on-the-job work experience, in a variety of functions, with part-time study. The main professional body that offers qualifications in insurance is the Chartered Insurance Institute (CII). To gain chartered status as an insurer, insurance practitioner or insurance broker, you need at least five years' relevant work experience and to have passed a CII-approved qualification, such as the Advanced Diploma in Insurance. You also need to commit to an ongoing programme of continuing professional development (CPD).

Finding vacancies

Employers advertise details of their graduate training schemes on their own websites. Vacancies are also advertised by specialist recruitment agencies, on many specialist and general online job sites, and in the appointments sections of certain daily newspapers.

While at university, or as a recent graduate, you can access information about potential employers and current graduate vacancies through your university careers service. Further information about the help available through university careers services is provided in Chapter three.

Sources of further information

The Chartered Insurance Institute (CII) – tel: 020 8989 8464. www.cii.co.uk

The Chartered Institute of Loss Adjusters – tel: 020 7337 9960. www.cila.co.uk

Financial Services Skills Council – the Sector Skills Council for financial services, accountancy and finance. Tel: 0845 257 3772. www.fssc.org.uk

Lloyds – tel: 020 7327 1000. www.lloyds.com

Stockbroker

The London Stock Exchange is a marketplace where companies can raise money by issuing and selling shares to individual and institutional investors. The Government also raises money there by selling bonds. Many individuals buy stocks and shares, many more have investments made on their behalf by the banks, building societies, pension funds and others who hold their money.

Stockbrokers, also known as dealers, advise clients, buy and sell stocks and shares on their behalf, and help clients manage their investments. They need to research the stock market and take advice from investment analysts, as well as regularly reviewing the performance of their clients' portfolios. Most contact with clients is carried out over the phone or by letter, while trading is done mainly over the phone or internet. Stockbrokers work long hours in a high-pressure environment. Firms of stockbrokers range from small firms to large international securities houses with hundreds of employees.

Market makers, also known as traders, are stockbrokers who act like wholesalers within the stock market by buying and selling stocks and shares on behalf of their own firm. They speculate on the potential supply and demand of particular shares, with the aim of selling the shares they buy at a profit. This involves researching the financial press and other sources of market information, consulting investment analysts and deciding the selling price of their shares. It's a high-pressured role that needs sound judgement and the ability to make quick decisions.

Other specialist roles relating to the stock market include those working in: **corporate finance** – raising finance for companies by issuing new shares; **mergers and acquisitions** – advising client companies and arranging finance for such activities; and **fund management** – managing investments for institutional clients. There are also openings to become **investment analysts** or **researchers**. These are specialists who provide market intelligence to brokers, market makers and institutional investors.

Entry qualifications

Any degree subject may be acceptable, but for some roles, employers prefer degrees with a high mathematical content. A background in law, economics, finance or business would be useful. Alternatively, analysts may have degrees related to the area in which they want to specialise – surveying for property analysts, geology or chemistry for those specialising in petrochemicals.

Regardless of which area of work you enter, you will need to be numerate, articulate and able to assimilate lots of data quickly and accurately. You must have a good analytical mind and plenty of stamina. You should also be interested in current affairs. Above all, you must have the social skills necessary if you are to form good relationships with clients and earn their confidence.

Training and career development

A graduate training programme is likely to combine classroom training with on-the-job experience. Many roles in this sector are regulated by the Financial Services Authority (FSA), which means to work unsupervised you must have passed an 'appropriate' exam as detailed by the FSSC (the Financial Services Skills Council). Even in unregulated roles, for example in compliance (which involves ensuring the organisation and its employees comply with all relevant regulations), employers are still likely to expect you to gain a qualification from the FSSC's 'recommended' exam list. The Chartered Institute for Securities and Investment (CISI) is the main professional body for this sector and offers relevant exams, as does the CFA Society of the UK.

Finding vacancies

Contact the London Stock Exchange for details of member firms who are likely to advertise vacancies and details of any graduate training schemes they run on their own websites. The CISI website also lists a selection of graduate schemes as well as career events. Vacancies are also advertised by specialist recruitment agencies, on many specialist and general online job sites, and in the appointments sections of certain daily newspapers.

While at university, or as a recent graduate, you can access information about potential employers and current graduate vacancies through your university careers service. Further information about the help that is available through university careers services is provided in Chapter three.

Sources of further information

Chartered Institute for Securities & Investment (CISI) – tel: 020 7645 0600. www.cisi.org

CFA Society of the UK – tel: 020 7280 9620. www.cfauk.org

Financial Services Skills Council – the Sector Skills Council for financial services, accountancy and finance. Tel: 0845 257 3772. www.fssc.org.uk

The London Stock Exchange – tel: 020 7797 1000. www.londonstockexchange.com

Chapter twelve

Careers in heritage work

"Management has gone to her head"

Heritage work covers the very broad career area concerned with managing, conserving and making accessible our historical buildings, sites and artefacts. It is estimated that over 50,000 people work in jobs related to cultural heritage. While graduate-level opportunities tend to be of most relevance to those with history or related degrees, there are also some openings for graduates of any degree subject. This chapter covers:

- archivist

- archaeologist

- museum and art gallery work

- working for heritage organisations.

Archivist

Archivists collect and preserve records. Although most people think in terms of ancient documents, contemporary material is also stored for future use. Apart from documents, modern records can include microfilm, CDs and other digital material, and audio and video recordings. N.B. Because there is overlap between the work of archivists and that of librarians/information managers, your should also refer to Chapter fourteen.

As well as records from public organisations, such as government bodies, law courts and so on, archives may include private papers such as title deeds, family papers and the diaries and letters of notable people. As an archivist you'll be involved in the study and selection of material, deciding what is worth preserving for posterity. You will take responsibility for the preservation, arrangement and description of the material for future reference purposes. You'll be responsible for providing access to records for users, from academic researchers to members of the public, depending on the archive.

Most archivists work for central or local government. Major national archives include the National Archives at Kew, in London and the National Monuments Record Centre in Swindon. Local archives are situated around the country. There are also limited openings in other organisations, including professional institutions, universities, libraries, specialist museums, industry and research bodies.

Entry qualifications

Entry is possible with a good degree in any subject, and you will then need to take a postgraduate course in archives/records management – the Society of Archivists accredit courses. Relevant work experience – paid or unpaid – is often required before you start postgraduate studies.

Apart from a strong sense of history, you'll need to be curious and to enjoy painstaking research. Attention to detail, patience and good communication skills are also needed for this area of work.

Training and career development

Training is on the job, perhaps supplemented by short courses, such as those run by the Society of Archivists. The Society also offers a Registration Scheme for newly-qualified archivists. This involves compiling a portfolio and takes a minimum of three years to complete.

Finding vacancies

This is a very small profession. Only a small number of universities run postgraduate courses. Consequently, most employers with vacancies will target those institutions. You're most likely to find your first post either through your academic department, which will be in contact with most potential employers, or through your university careers service.

For a list of most of the UK's archives, see: www.nationalarchives.gov.uk/archon.

Sources of further information

Society of Archivists – tel: 01823 327030. www.archives.org.uk

Archaeologist

Archaeology is the study of our human past through physical remains. These range from buried cities to microscopic organisms. Archaeology involves far more than digging up artefacts on historic sites. The work of the archaeologist may start with trying to locate a site, which may entail careful research, such as the study of aerial photographs and the use of remote sensing methods. Plotting and analysing increasingly involves computer-based techniques. Geophysical procedures can also reveal much of the layout of the hidden remains before digging begins.

Once digging starts, the position of every object found has to be precisely plotted in three dimensions. The position of an object, both on the site and in relation to other finds, often reveals more than the object itself.

Many delicate artefacts are preserved in the soil or under water, and start to decay as soon as they are exposed to the air. Conservation – preserving and caring for objects so that they survive after excavation – is a vital part of archaeological work. Finds have to be catalogued, photographed, drawn (drawings often reveal details not seen in photographs) and examined. Artefacts are studied, physically and chemically, to find out how they were made and to identify the origin of the raw materials. They also have to be dated, using a range of radiocarbon and other techniques. As you can see, archaeology spans the arts and sciences. Conservation and the examination of artefacts are usually carried out in laboratories by staff with specialist skills. All aspects of the project must be written up.

Archaeologists tend to specialise in their work. Archaeologists can specialise geographically, chronologically (such as prehistory, Roman,

Anglo-Saxon etc) or technically (such as site surveying, excavation, studying artefacts and so on).

Archaeological excavations are often undertaken when new sites are being developed for building. As part of the planning consent, developers are required to allow archaeologists time to explore any areas of archaeological interest that may be revealed during excavations, or to record buildings of historical interest prior to redevelopment. Commercial archaeological companies are often contracted to undertake this work, which can also involve evaluation of proposed development sites, where the archaeologist's findings are taken into account in the planning process.

Entry qualifications

Archaeology is growing in popularity, and entry is competitive. While a degree in archaeology and related subjects is an advantage, entry is possible with non-related degree subjects. There are some specialisms in archaeology where a science degree, in subjects such as biology, botany, medicine, zoology and environmental science, may be relevant.

Postgraduate qualifications are available in a range of archaeological specialisms. A few of these have a scientific aspect, such as osteoarchaeology (bone identification), forensic archaeology and bioarchaeology.

Potential entrants should try to gain as much relevant work experience as possible. IT skills are also valuable. You also need patience, determination, good communication skills and the ability to work methodically.

Training and career development

Archaeology is a very small profession. If you aim to be an excavation archaeologist, you will need to work your way up through the ranks – from excavator to site assistant to supervisor and so on. The main qualification for advancement is practical experience.

Finding vacancies

Vacancies can be found on the British Archaeological Jobs & Resources (BAJR) website, at www.bajr.org. The Institute for Archaeologists issues a weekly bulletin to members by email (non-members can buy issues for a fee); see www.archaeologists.net. You're also likely to find suitable jobs advertised in *The Museums Journal*, while the *Archaeology Abroad Bulletin*, published annually, advertises fieldwork opportunities outside the UK (www.britarch.ac.uk/archabroad).

While at university, or if a recent graduate, you can access information about potential employers and current graduate vacancies through your university careers service. Further information about the help available through university careers services is provided in Chapter three.

Sources of further information

Council for British Archaeology – tel: 01904 671417.
www.britarch.ac.uk

Institute for Archaeologists – tel: 0118 378 6446.
www.archaeologists.net

Museum and art gallery work

Museums collect, document, preserve, exhibit, interpret and store materials of historical, scientific and cultural interest. Art galleries do the same for paintings, sculpture and other works of art. Some institutions are both a museum and an art gallery. Museums and art galleries are increasingly part of the leisure and tourism industry and aim to entertain as well as inform visitors. Displays are now far more imaginative than in the past – as demonstrated by the exhibitions mounted by the Natural History Museum in London, for example.

Because many aspects of the work are very similar, for the purpose of this chapter both types of institution are referred to as museums. There are four main types of museum: national, university, local authority and independent.

National museums: These are mainly government-funded, although most have to raise extra money through souvenir sales, sponsorship and so on. The national museums include the British Museum, the National Gallery, and various museums based across the country, such as National Railway Museum at York or, in Wales, the Big Pit National Coal Museum. Some museums, such as the Science Museum in London, may be of particular interest to science graduates.

University museums: Most university museums are departmental collections used for teaching and research. There is a handful of large university museums that are open to the public and employ full-time curators, such as the Ashmolean in Oxford.

Local authority museums: These range from famous museums such the Museum of London or the Roman Baths in Bath, through to small museums of local history with only one or two staff.

Independent museums: The largest growing group is the independent museums, which need to be commercially successful. They include tourist attractions like the Ironbridge Gorge Museum, as well as hundreds of small, special interest museums.

The job roles available in museums are varied and include curator, education officer and exhibition officer. Larger museums, particularly those that operate as major tourist attractions, employ operational managers, responsible for day-to-day general management and financial affairs.

Curators look after the museum's collections. As a curator, you'd be responsible for acquiring objects and for researching, cataloguing, storing, displaying and interpreting them. In the largest museums these would be your only duties and you might be able to specialise. In most museums, however, curators are also involved in managing the museum or their department within it, which may include managing staff and various administrative duties. Curators may hold other specific responsibilities too, such as fund raising, security and publicity.

Exhibition officers work with curators on the permanent exhibitions and may take responsibility for temporary exhibitions, both those put on by the museum itself, or visiting exhibitions. Duties may involve everything from planning to publicity.

Education officers organise and deliver activities for groups of young people visiting the museum, and in schools and colleges. Education officers may prepare teaching materials for school projects, hold workshops for teachers on how to make the best of the museum, organise and run holiday events for young people and give talks.

Entry qualifications

To become a curator or art gallery keeper in a national or local authority museum you'll normally need a degree (in any subject, although applicants with relevant degrees may have an advantage) and a postgraduate qualification in museum studies or a related subject. Independent museums may be more flexible in the qualifications they require, depending on the post, but it is very helpful to have relevant postgraduate qualifications. Such museums will also tend to look for business skills.

For working as an exhibition officer, a relevant postgraduate qualification may be required. To become an education officer, a teaching or community education background is usually needed.

It is increasingly important for all that you have prior relevant work experience, perhaps as a volunteer.

Training and career development

The largest museums have well-established career structures. Your career may lead from assistant curator/keeper through ranks of increasing seniority up to director with responsibility for running the whole museum. However, administration and management jobs are increasingly seen as distinct from that of curator. The directors of some national museums have been appointed from outside the museum world, but most senior post-holders, including the directors of most museums, begin their career as curators. Elsewhere you are most likely to progress your career by moving from one museum to another. Some posts are on a fixed-term basis.

Finding vacancies

There is a vacancy search facility on the Museums Association website (see below) and positions are advertised in the Association's *Museums Journal*. Also look in the national press, and regional papers for jobs in local authority museums.

While at university, or as a recent graduate, you can access information about potential employers and current graduate vacancies through your university careers service. Further information about the help available through university careers services is provided in Chapter three.

Sources of further information

Associations of Independent Museums (AIM) – tel: 02392 587751. www.aim-museums.co.uk

Creative & Cultural Skills – the Sector Skills Council covering cultural heritage. Tel: 01274 391056. www.ccskills.org.uk

The Museums Association – tel: 020 7426 6910. www.museumsassociation.org

Working for heritage organisations

The range of historic sites across the UK means that there is a wide variety of employment opportunities. For example, running and preserving somewhere like Dover Castle in Kent – with its many visitors each day of the year, who want to be entertained and informed, directed and refreshed – is very different from the work of a trust restoring a canal for navigation, rebuilding locks, clearing rubbish and mud from the waterway and making decisions about fishing and boating.

Some job opportunities require specialist professional qualifications, such as surveying, architecture or archive work, for example. There are also opportunities in general management and administration, including in publicity, public relations, catering management, financial management and so on. Staff are based at head offices and at particular heritage sites.

The main organisations involved in running heritage sites are listed below.

English Heritage – runs many of the main historic sites, such as Stonehenge, as well as smaller sites, e.g. Iron Age villages, ruined monasteries etc. English Heritage employs over 1,600 staff. There are separate government bodies responsible for the upkeep of heritage sites in other parts of the UK.

National Trust – owns many historic buildings and parks, as well as unspoiled countryside and coastline. The Trust employs over 4,000 staff.

The Churches of England, Wales and Scotland – own magnificent cathedrals and churches, which have become major tourist attractions.

Local authorities, trusts or **charities** own many other historic sites, and, of course, there are many historic houses open to the public that are in **private ownership**. Some historic properties are operated by **commercial companies**.

Entry qualifications

Entry qualifications vary according to the job role. Some opportunities may ask for a degree in a specific subject. Prior relevant experience and a demonstrable interest in heritage is helpful, if not essential.

Training and career development

Training depends on the job role. On-the-job training is generally supplemented with short courses or possibly the option to take further qualifications.

English Heritage runs a Historic Environment Traineeship scheme, providing training and experience. The degree subjects that are listed as being relevant for entry to the scheme include environmental sciences. You can find out more on their website.

Finding vacancies

You can find job vacancies for English Heritage through their website, listed below, and for the National Trust on www.ntjobs.org.uk. For local authority vacancies, see www.LGjobs.com.

Sources of further information

Cadw – the Welsh Assemby's historic environment service. Tel: 01443 336000. www.cadw.wales.gov.uk

Creative & Cultural Skills – the Sector Skills Council that covers cultural heritage. Tel: 020 7015 1800. www.ccskills.org.uk www.creative-choices.co.uk

English Heritage – tel: 0870 333 1181. www.english-heritage.org.uk

National Trust – tel: 01793 817400. www.nationaltrust.org.uk

Chapter thirteen

Careers in leisure, travel and tourism

Although the leisure, travel and tourism sector offers plenty of openings, few of the jobs are exclusively for graduates. You can expect to compete for jobs with non-graduates with relevant work experience. However, you should find that the transferable skills acquired during your degree studies help to give you an advantage. Some of the larger employers do recruit graduates specifically, and run graduate training programmes.

This chapter briefly describes the following careers:

- arts administrator
- catering manager
- conference and exhibition manager
- entertainments manager
- events manager
- hotel manager
- tour operator and related work
- tourism officer
- visitor attraction/holiday centre manager.

Arts administrator

Arts administrators organise events such as concerts, plays, art exhibitions and festivals. Employers may be theatre and dance companies, community arts organisations and local authorities.

The responsibilities of the job include:

- planning seasonal programmes
- organising individual events
- booking venues
- engaging performers
- publicity
- negotiating grants from public funds and commercial sponsorship
- day-to-day administration.

The exact nature of the work will depend largely on the size of the organisation for which you work. For example, in a large organisation you might specialise in marketing, whereas in a small organisation you could be responsible for all the activities listed above.

Catering manager

Catering managers have to plan, organise and manage food and beverage services. They are mainly employed by hotels, restaurants, businesses, hospitals, care homes, cruise ships, holiday centres, educational institutions, conference centres and other places where large numbers of people need to eat and drink. Catering managers have to achieve customer satisfaction while balancing quality and cost. They are also responsible for maintaining high standards of cleanliness and food hygiene. Many graduates who go into catering management have gained relevant experience through doing part-time or seasonal jobs at weekends and during university vacations.

Conference and exhibition manager

Exhibition and conference centres, and some larger hotels, employ managers to organise and direct all the appropriate services for the running of events. These can range from one-day events involving a few dozen delegates to events attended by several thousand people over three or four days. The latter may combine an exhibition with a programme of workshops, lectures and other meetings.

The manager has overall responsibility for ensuring that all the services run smoothly – delegate reception, accommodation and catering, lecture rooms and their seating, exhibitions, audiovisual equipment, press office, entertainment and so on. The manager leads a team of people, but will have overall responsibility for planning, for ensuring that everything runs smoothly (and that problems are resolved satisfactorily as they arise) and that the event is profitable.

Entertainments manager

Entertainments managers are employed by organisations such as holiday centre operators, cruise companies, hotel and leisure businesses, and local authorities. The work involves organising and delivering a range of entertainments, which, depending on the setting, could include children's activities, games nights, quizzes, discos, cabarets and stage shows. Duties may include booking performers and organising individual events, dealing with publicity, managing the finances, and taking responsibility for matters such as health and safety.

Events manager

Events managers are the people who take responsibility for organising anything from festivals or outdoor concerts to horticultural shows, sporting events, weddings, private parties, charity fundraising balls or corporate hospitality functions. They work mainly for specialist events management companies.

The responsibilities of event managers are wide. They may include finding a suitable venue, sorting out advertising and publicity, making sure that legal regulations are met, negotiating with contractors and suppliers (such as staging suppliers or caterers), dealing with security and car parking, and looking after the finances.

Hotel manager

As a hotel manager you would be responsible for running every aspect of a hotel. This includes managing staff; organising the furnishings; maintenance and cleaning services; the running of the restaurant, bars and the reception area; dealing with customer complaints and unexpected problems; and, above all, being responsible for the financial performance of the business. In a large hotel you would have a management team with several heads of departments. In a small hotel you would carry out all the management tasks and even give a helping hand if any staff were absent.

Tour operator and related work

The larger tour operators recruit graduates for head office functions. Vacancies are mainly in marketing, information technology, sales, finance and contracting. Working in head office in the job role of contractor, for example, you would have to choose resorts, and negotiate with airlines, coach companies, hotels and villa owners, getting the best possible prices for your company. Finance is critical to the success of a travel company, because profit margins are normally very low for package holidays and budgets must be monitored very closely. Apart from the large, well known travel companies, there may also be opportunities with the smaller, specialist tour operators.

To gain some relevant experience, you might choose to be a **travel courier** for a season or two. As a courier you look after holiday travellers, usually while travelling by coach. You care for your party throughout the trip – welcome them, give a commentary on places of interest during the tour, liaise with hotels and restaurants, deal with problems and emergencies as they arise, and generally ensure that your clients have a trouble-free and enjoyable trip.

Another option that will provide experience is to work for a tour operator as a **resort representative** (often known as 'reps'). They do similar work to couriers but are based in a resort, where they are likely to look after clients in several hotels, dealing with problems and selling excursions etc. Reps are usually employed by the season.

Tourism officer

Tourism officers are mainly employed by local authorities, but may also work for other public bodies and private organisations. They are responsible for marketing the attractions of their particular region, or their visitor attraction, with the aim of increasing visitor numbers. The work may involve running visitor services, such as tourist centres, and dealing with providers of visitor services, such as tourist attractions, hotels and tour operators. As a tourism officer, you would be responsible for strategic planning and organising new attractions, festivals, fairs and other events to attract visitors. You would also be involved in producing publicity materials, running a website, writing press releases, and possibly involved in commissioning DVD and television commercials.

On the administrative side, you would also be managing staff, and writing and presenting reports for your employer.

Visitor attraction/Holiday centre manager

Visitor attractions, ranging from theme parks and heritage centres to holiday centres, all need a range of management staff. Large operations employ managers based at individual attractions, to manage the various on-site facilities, as well as at head office, to deal with overall company strategy, future planning, marketing, human resources, finances and so on. You can read more about careers that are particularly related to heritage work in Chapter twelve.

Entry qualifications

As mentioned at the start of this chapter, having a degree is not essential for the jobs described. However, some of the larger companies do run graduate recruitment programmes. If applying for graduate vacancies as a science graduate, you are likely to be competing with applicants holding degrees in more relevant subjects to this career area than you, which may give them an initial advantage for some positions. However, your personal qualities, enthusiasm and commitment are important and will be of interest to employers. It would also help your application if you have been able to gain some relevant experience, at any level, which will also provide you with industry contacts and a reference.

If you are competing against non-graduates, as a graduate you should have developed a range of skills, such as communication and problem solving, that employers value. Again, any relevant work experience will help you.

For some jobs, such as conference and exhibition management, employers look for a few years' relevant prior experience. Where relevant postgraduate courses are available, it may be worth considering taking such a course prior to entry. For example, there are some postgraduate arts administration and management courses, which may help you gain entry into that area of work.

Training and career development

For some jobs, including hotel management, some larger employers run graduate training programmes, which provide structured training over one to two years. In other organisations, and in other career areas, such as arts administration, training is mainly on the job, supplemented by relevant short courses. Larger employers may offer scope for career progression within the organisation. In smaller organisations, promotion to a more senior role may require moving to a different employer.

Finding vacancies

Opportunities with local authorities can be viewed on www.LGjobs. com. Depending on you particular career area of interest, you can find vacancies advertised in magazines such as *The Stage* (www.thestage. co.uk), *Arts Professional* (www.artsprofessional.co.uk), *Travel Trade Gazette* (www.ttglive.com) and *Travel Weekly* (www.travelweekly.co.uk).

While at university, or if a recent graduate, you can access information about potential employers and current graduate vacancies through your university careers service. Further information about the help available through university careers services is provided in Chapter three.

Sources of further information

Creative & Cultural Skills – the Sector Skills Council for crafts, cultural heritage, design, literature, music, performing and visual arts. Tel: 020 7015 1800. www.ccskills.org.uk

Institute of Hospitality – the professional body for hospitality, leisure and tourism professionals. Tel: 020 8661 4900. www.instituteofhospitality.org

Institute of Travel & Tourism (ITT) – tel: 0844 499 5653. www.itt.co.uk

People 1st – the Sector Skills Council for hospitality, leisure, travel and tourism. Tel: 01895 817000. www.people1st.co.uk

Springboard UK – promotes hospitality, leisure, travel and tourism careers, and provides careers information. Tel: 020 7497 8654. www.springboarduk.net

Chapter fourteen

Careers in library and information work

We live in an age of information. Managing it, organising it, storing it and making it accessible is the task of librarians and other information specialists. Apart from paper-based material, staff working in this field deal with film, video/DVD, photographic, microfiche, audio, CD-ROM and other electronic records.

This chapter covers the jobs of:

- librarian/information manager – including information scientist
- researcher.

Librarian/Information manager

The traditional picture of a librarian is generally someone who looks after shelves of books and lends these out to borrowers. This isn't a real reflection of the job today, which should be more realistically thought of as information management.

In Britain alone, we create huge masses of information. Apart from books (novels and non-fiction), newspapers and journals, policy documents and records are produced by every government department and agency, reports are produced by businesses and other organisations, research papers are produced by academic researchers, and so on.

Such material must be managed in a way that enables data to be easily accessed when needed. Some material must be kept for years for legal, administrative, financial and other purposes. Some is of historical significance and must be retained in permanent archives. All these decisions and responsibilities fall to the librarian or information manager.

The work of librarians and information managers – who are sometimes called information specialists – is very similar. The particular responsibilities vary depending on the situation – such as looking after information resources in a reference library or a specialist library in business or industry, or for a professional body, for example. Keeping records electronically is an increasingly important part of the work, and managing digital cataloguing systems.

Librarians in public lending libraries are responsible for the selection, purchase, cataloguing and arrangement of books, periodicals, DVDs, CDs, information packs and other materials. Some librarians organise special services such as mobile libraries, children's activities and business sections.

Academic librarians serve both staff and students. In collaboration with their academic colleagues, they select materials to support the study and research taking place in the institution. Many academic librarians specialise in a particular subject area.

In some jobs, you may be involved in creating indexing and suitable storing systems. You may need to ensure that anyone authorised to do so can easily access the information you look after. You may have to handle internal and external requests for information.

Information scientist

This role is very similar to that of an information manager, but the emphasis of the work is often in a specialist field, such as scientific, technical, legal, economic or commercial. Information scientists may work for research organisations, professional institutions, employers, government agencies and other bodies. Besides managing the information resources and helping users locate the information they need, information scientists may develop new databases, conduct information searches and write reports, produce summaries or abstracts of information and analyse statistical information. They could also be responsible for online data services such as intranets (internal corporate websites).

Entry qualifications

Those whose first degree is not in librarianship, information management or information science will need to take a postgraduate course, accredited by the Chartered Institute of Library and Information Professionals (CILIP). Relevant work experience is often required for entry to a postgraduate course.

People working in information management need good organisational and communication skills, and to be confident with ICT.

Training and career development

Staff may work towards chartered membership of CILIP. With experience, it is possible to gain promotion to management-level roles, or move into a more specialist information role.

Finding vacancies

CILIP publishes the *Library and Information Gazette*, which carries professional-level vacancies (and can be accessed online). You can also find relevant vacancies on www.lisjobnet.com or, for local government, see www.LGtalent.com (also carries careers information).

While at university, or if a recent graduate, you can access current graduate vacancies through your university careers service. Further details about the advice and information available through university careers services are provided in Chapter three.

Sources of further information

Aslib, The Association for Information Management – tel: 020 7253 3349. www.aslib.com

Chartered Institute of Library and Information Professionals (CILIP) – carries lists of accredited courses and vacancies for graduate training positions. Tel: 020 7255 0500. www.cilip.org.uk

Chartered Institute of Library and Information Professionals (CILIP) (in Wales) – tel: 01970 622174. www.dis.aber.ac.uk/cilip_w

Researcher

Researchers are used by a variety of organisations from government departments to trade unions, from political parties to market research companies.

In government you would normally be working within a government department and handling external and internal research enquiries, which could come from colleagues, other government departments, academics, local councils, regional development agencies and members of the public. A lot of the work would be desk research in libraries or via the internet, but you would use a variety of other techniques including surveys.

You could also find yourself briefing, orally or in writing, senior colleagues and government ministers on the research evidence that you have found. On occasions you might have to present papers at conferences.

Social researchers focus particularly on social issues, such as poverty, housing and changing social attitudes. They may be employed by public bodies, trades unions, social research bodies and commercial firms, including market research agencies. After getting a brief from your client you might use a variety of research techniques. These could include desk research, quantitative and qualitative research, questionnaires and so on. With some agencies this could include developing and testing new theories.

There is also political research. Political researchers generally work for political parties or individual Members of Parliament (MPs), where research may be one element of their role in assisting the MP. Apart from researching political issues in depth, you would monitor the media and Hansard (which reports parliamentary debates verbatim) to spot emerging political issues and to identify possible lines of attack that could be used against your party's rivals. You will also prepare briefs and policy papers as well as ghost write articles and speeches for your party's MPs.

Although political researchers are usually associated with the House of Commons, there are also opportunities working within the House of Lords, and for politicians in the European Parliament and devolved UK parliaments.

Entry qualifications

Although any degree is normally acceptable, for some areas of research, employers may prefer social science graduates.

Training and career development

Training tends to be on the job. Working as a political researcher is often used as a stepping stone towards becoming an MP or senior party official.

Finding vacancies

While at university, or if a recent graduate, you can access information about potential employers and current graduate vacancies through your university careers service. Further details about the services available through university careers services are provided in Chapter three.

Sources of further information

(MRS) Market Research Society – tel: 020 7490 4911.
www.mrs.org.uk

NatCen (National Centre for Social Research) – tel: 020 7250 1866.
www.natcen.ac.uk

Office for National Statistics – tel: 0845 601 3034. www.ons.gov.uk

The Social Research Association – tel: 020 7388 2391.
www.the-sra.org.uk

Chapter fifteen

Careers in management

In this chapter we'll look at the basic role of a manager and describe some of the management functions in which you could make a career:

- accounting and finance
- buying
- facilities management
- human resources (HR) or personnel management
- logistics
- management services and management consultancy

- marketing
- product development
- production
- sales.

A manager is responsible for running an organisation, a section of an organisation, or taking responsibility of a particular function across the organisation. Whether you are managing a manufacturing company, a business that provides a service or a government department, the principles are the same. You must develop products or services that satisfy your customers' needs while controlling costs, and ensure they are available when and where they are needed. As public service is covered in Chapter sixteen, this chapter concentrates on business organisations.

The traditional structure of management comprises line managers who head a section of a department or a whole department, who, in turn, report to senior managers who plan, coordinate and supervise the activities of all departments so that they work together effectively. At senior management level, the work involves making policy decisions, setting strategy and long-term planning. No two organisations are exactly the same in how they are structured – some have much 'flatter' hierachies (fewer levels of staff) than others.

In some organisations you will find project managers, who lead a team that has been created to undertake a specific job or project for a specific time period. One of the biggest differences of working in a project management role is that you may not have responsibility for a permanent team of your own staff.

However, most managers are concerned with long-term operational management. This involves implementing policy decisions and organising resources so that the activities of the business run smoothly and profitably. As an operational manager, you will typically:

- set your team's objectives and targets
- plan the work of the department or section
- attend planning and other meetings
- prepare budgets and get them agreed by senior management
- ensure you have the resources that your department needs and keep to agreed budgets

- keep records and monitor them against targets and budgets

- report progress to senior management

- train, develop, supervise and motivate your staff

- monitor the quality of the work done by your team

- monitor individual performance, making sure that targets are met

- keep your staff informed about what's going on within the organisation

- constantly seek better ways of doing things

- solve problems when they arise

- liaise with managers in other departments

- liaise with suppliers and customers, as appropriate.

Management functions

The following section outlines the main areas of business in which managers are employed.

Accounting and finance

Every business must keep full details of all its financial transactions and have them audited each year. To control the money going in and out of a business, each department works to a budget. Departmental managers need to know, monthly or even more often, how they are doing against their budgets through a system of 'management accounting'. **Management accountants** are employed within the organisation to collect and analyse the organisation's financial information in order to forecast results, create business plans, control budgets, prepare reports and so on. **Financial accountants** oversee the financial transactions of an organisation. This includes managing the payment of wages, taxes, invoices, preparing accounts, managing investments and carrying out internal audits.

The openings for graduates in finance are discussed in more detail in Chapter eleven.

Buying

All organisations need to buy goods and materials to go about their business, and this is the role of the buyer. Manufacturers buy raw materials and components to make their products. This is not just a matter of negotiating a good price, but also of securing consistent quality and guaranteed delivery times.

Retailers buy goods for resale, either direct from manufacturers or from wholesalers. Retail buyers are concerned with recognising and predicting customer buying trends and finding the products to satisfy them. In service industries, buyers are responsible for acquiring all those supplies necessary for their business to operate – for instance, in hotels they might buy everything from buildings to bedding.

Facilities management

In larger organisations, facilities managers take responsibility for looking after the buildings and the services provided within them. They make sure that the buildings are well maintained, and organise services such as cleaning, security, air conditioning, heating and communications. Facilities managers also have major responsibility if any moves to new premises are scheduled.

Human resources (HR) or Personnel management

A business must recruit, train and develop staff for every function. It must also care for everyone's health, safety and welfare, make sure that people are paid fairly, deal with equal opportunities and much more. This is the role of the HR or personnel manager. Many HR managers, particularly in large organisations, specialise in specific areas, such as recruitment or training.

Logistics

Logistics is concerned with making sure goods, materials or components are in the right place at the right time. For example, in manufacturing, after goods are made, they are traditionally stored until needed. Then, when required, they are distributed in such a way that they reach the customer on time and in perfect condition. Customers may be anywhere in the world. Controlling costs by careful route planning is vital. Reliability of delivery is also a responsibility of the logistics manager; goods and components often need to be delivered to a production line only a few hours before they are needed, or delivered to a supermarket and put on display. So late deliveries will do your business reputation no good at all!

Management services and management consultancy

Rather than managing an organisation or department directly, staff working in management services and management consultancy use specialist skills and expertise to find solutions to business problems, such as improving productivity.

There are many specialisms within **management services**. These include method study – observing how tasks are performed, before developing and putting in place new, more efficient ways of working; management control – making sure that organisations conform to relevant regulations; and information management – such as analysing information needs and implementing appropriate ICT systems.

Management consultants advise organisations how to manage their affairs more effectively. A management consultancy company may be brought in to solve a specific problem, to find ways to improve existing operations or to conduct feasibility studies. After investigation and analysis, management consultants will recommend actions to be taken.

Marketing

Marketing managers identify markets for existing and new products. They might suggest ideas for new products that need to be developed. They investigate potential new markets and existing markets to find out what new products could be introduced. The marketing team will either conduct or commission market research. Marketing managers work with specialists to create an identity or 'image' for the product through carefully thought out brand names, packaging, advertising and other promotional campaigns. Marketing managers need to be aware of what their competitors are doing and monitor the performance of products in terms of sales, customer satisfaction and profitability.

Product development

This concerns creating new or improved products. If you're in business to make such things as ready-made foods, pharmaceuticals, computers or toiletries, you will have research and development teams of scientists and technologists. If your products are items such as fabrics, furniture, clothing or jewellery then designers will create these. The production development team must liaise with marketing, in order to design products that meet customer needs, and with production, to ensure that the designs are practical to make.

Production

Products are made in many ways. These include computer-controlled production lines for making items such as cars, continuous process plants, such as oil and chemical refineries and assembly lines in which people build up parts into finished products. Or products may be 'one-offs' and made to order – from a specialist tooling machine to a cruise liner. It is the role of the production manager to ensure that the operations run as smoothly and as efficiently as possible. The job includes responsibility for staff, maintenance, planning the workload and of course, dealing with any problems that are causing delays in manufacturing as quickly as possible.

Sales

Selling is about persuading people to buy your products. Sales managers call on potential and existing customers. They identify customer needs through discussion and then show how the company's product can satisfy that customer's needs better than those of its competitors. Promotion could be to regional sales manager, looking after a team of sales staff. At head office, management staff in the sales department also take responsibility for making sure that new orders are processed efficiently, queries are dealt with and that any problems are resolved.

Entry qualifications

In most companies, it is possible for staff to work their way up into management positions, through a successful work track record and gaining qualifications through part-time study. Larger organisations also recruit graduates into trainee management posts. Any degree subject is normally acceptable, although for some specialist areas of management, a relevant degree may be required or preferred.

Work experience (from vacation work, work placements linked to your studies and so on) is especially valued. If you are attracted to working in business, it is worth remembering that foreign language skills could also be valuable.

Apart from the above, potential employers will be particularly interested in your personal qualities and skills. Managers need to be flexible, and able to constantly reprioritise their work, because problems can arise at any moment and must often be dealt with at once. So, if you like getting your head down to concentrate on one thing at a time without interruption, then management may not be for you! Managers must also be able to motivate those around them; effective managers earn the respect and cooperation of their team.

In addition, to be an effective manager you need to be self-confident, have the ability to build up good working relationships with others, and be able to communicate clearly and persuasively, orally and in writing. You need good problem-solving and organisational skills, and to be capable of working to deadlines and under pressure. You must be able to argue your point of view persuasively, and yet be willing to listen and learn, and make compromises when appropriate.

Training and career development

There are two usual entry routes into a management career – through a graduate management training scheme, usually run only by large organisations, and direct entry into a particular post.

Graduate management training programmes usually take around 18-24 months and typically combine skills training and project work. You're likely to spend time in a number of functions. This will help you to understand how the business works as a whole, and to find out which specialist area is best suited to your interests and aptitudes.

After the training programme, you may be expected to study towards professional qualifications, such as those offered by the Chartered Management Institute or the Institute of Operations Management. If you are moving into a specialist area you may study towards the qualifications of the appropriate professional body, such as the Chartered Institute of Marketing, the Chartered Institute of Management Accountants or the Chartered Institute of Personnel and Development. You'll usually get day release and possibly some study leave before your examinations, and your employer will pay your fees and other expenses – but most of your study will be in your free time.

If you are a direct entrant, you will undergo 'induction training' to learn about the organisation, the goods or services it provides, its systems and so on. You will then start your job. Initially, you will work under close supervision – being trained on the job. You are likely to go on courses from time to time. Depending on your function, you may also be able to study part time for a relevant professional qualification.

Whatever your entry route, as you become more senior you will become increasingly concerned with coordinating the activities of different functions, and so move into general management. You may consider gaining a masters degree in business administration (MBA).

Finding vacancies

Vacancies may be listed on employers websites and in national and regional newspapers. While at university, or if a recent graduate, you can access information about potential employers and current graduate vacancies through your university careers service. Further details about the services available through university careers services are provided in Chapter three.

Sources of further information

Chartered Management Institute - tel: 01536 204222.
www.managers.org.uk

Institute of Leadership and Management - tel: 01543 266867.
www.i-l-m.com

Institute of Operations Management - tel: 01536 740105.
www.iomnet.org.uk

There are many chartered institutes and professional bodies representing all aspects of management; search online for those that are relevant to your particular interests.

Chapter sixteen

Careers in public service

There are two broad areas of public service in the UK – the Civil Service and local government. Further afield, there are the various institutions of the European Union. This chapter looks at all three career areas.

Civil Service

There are more than 170 government departments and agencies, employing nearly half a million people in the UK. Collectively, the Civil Service is Britain's largest employer of graduates. It is responsible for a huge range of services that affect almost every area of our lives – from education and employment to transport and the court services. Contrary to some assumptions, only one in five civil servants works in London.

Graduates may expect to join at executive officer level. At this level, you would normally be responsible for putting government policy into practice. You would look after the day-to-day operations in your particular area of work. Your duties may include:

- supervising a team
- producing reports
- giving presentations
- managing information
- liaising with people in other departments and agencies
- undertaking research
- dealing with members of the public.

At more senior levels, staff are responsible, under government ministers, for formulating and carrying out the policy of the government of the day. The focus of the work is on policy making. Activities can include:

- researching and analysing policy options

- consulting and negotiating with people in other organisations

- developing systems to implement policies

- drafting replies to Parliamentary questions

- drafting new laws

- supporting ministers in departmental management.

Entry qualifications

Graduates enter the Civil Service either through the recruitment schemes of the individual departments or agencies, or apply for the Fast Stream entry route.

Fast Stream recruitment is aimed at those with exceptional ability and the potential to progress quickly. The minimum entry requirement is a second class degree, in any subject, although some more specialised areas of government require particular degree subjects, such as science or a numerate subject. In the recruitment process, the selectors will be looking particularly at the skills and personal qualities applicants have to offer. These include excellent communication and leadership skills, the ability to develop good relationships, and to be able to think flexibly and handle pressure.

The Graduate Fast Stream is subdivided into five areas: central departments (i.e. major government departments other than the Foreign and Commonwealth Office); the Diplomatic Service; Houses of Parliament; European Fast Stream; and science and engineering. This latter area is open to holders of degrees in science, engineering, maths and computing. Entrants into this career area may be based in the Ministry of Defence, undertaking research or procurement for technically-advanced projects, or in policy development. Alternatively, they could work within the Department for Business, Innovation and Skills.

There are also a few, more specialist Fast Stream schemes: the Economists Fast Stream, Statisticians Fast Stream, HR Fast Stream and Technology in Business (which focuses on IT). Details of these schemes and further information on the Graduate Fast Stream are found on the Fast Stream website, listed below.

For mainstream recruitment, there is a wide range of opportunities across all areas of government. Each department sets its own entry criteria.

Often, departments don't specify particular educational qualifications, as they select applicants against the competencies and skills required for the particular job.

For more information visit the Civil Service website or individual departmental websites listed below

Training and career development

Most Fast Streamers begin their careers with a series of placements or 'postings' – different jobs within their departments. Each posting lasts around 12 or 18 months, after which entrants move on to another project or area of work. There are also secondment opportunities, which could include working in another government department, or in business or industry. Entrants also receive about 15 days formal training a year, and there may be the opportunity to gain professional qualifications through part-time study or distance learning. Eventually, Fast Streamers either work in researching and developing government policy, operational delivery of services to the public, or in corporate services, such as human resources or finance.

For staff at executive officer level, training is mostly on the job, although departments and agencies run management development training to improve the promotion prospects of suitable staff. You may be considered for specialist training if you show a particular aptitude. Once you have a year's service, you may apply for the in-service Fast Stream.

Finding vacancies

Civil Service vacancies are found on the websites listed below. N.B. The NHS employs its own managers, separately from the civil servants in the Department of Health.

While at university, or if a recent graduate, you can access current graduate vacancies through your university careers service. Further details about the advice and information available through university careers services are provided in Chapter three.

Information about prison officers is included in Chapter seventeen.

Sources of further information

Civil Service Fast Stream Development Programme – tel: 01276 400333. www.civilservice.gov.uk/faststream

For vacancies across all departments, visit:
www.civilservice.gov.uk/jobs

Civil Service main departments and agencies include:

Crown Prosecution Service - brings criminals to trial. www.cps.gov.uk

Department for Business, Innovation & Skills - www.bis.gov.uk

Department for Culture, Media and Sports - www.culture.gov.uk

Department of Education - www.education.gov.uk

Department for Environment, Food and Rural Affairs -
www.defra.gov.uk

Department of Health - www.dh.gov.uk

Department for International Development - provides overseas aid
and assistance. www.dfid.gov.uk

Department for Transport - www.dft.gov.uk

Department for Work and Pensions - www.dwp.gov.uk

Foreign and Commonwealth Office - overseas relations.
www.fco.gov.uk

GCHQ Government Communications Headquarters -
www.gchq.gov.uk

Health and Safety Executive - www.hse.gov.uk

HM Revenue and Customs - assesses and collects taxes, excise duties,
VAT, etc. www.hmrc.gov.uk

HM Treasury - public revenues/expenditure and the financial system.
www.hm-treasury.gov.uk

Home Office - immigration and passports, drugs policy, counter-
terrorism and the police. www.homeoffice.gov.uk

Ministry of Defence - www.mod.uk

Ministry of Justice - www.justice.gov.uk

Office for National Statistics - www.ons.gov.uk

NHS Graduate Management Training Scheme -
www.nhsleadtheway.co.uk

Local government

Local government is concerned with providing services to the community. In career terms, it is a group of several hundred employers throughout the UK.

Services provided by local government authorities include:

- education
- environmental health
- fire and rescue service
- highways (building and repairs, traffic management, street lights, pavements, snow clearing)
- housing
- libraries
- police
- recreation, leisure, arts and museums
- social services
- strategic and local planning
- tourism promotion
- trading standards (consumer protection)
- transport
- waste and recycling services
- youth and community services, including, in England, the Connexions service, which provides careers guidance and personal support on a range of other issues to young people. (N.B. Connexions services may be provided directly by local government or contracted out - see Chapter eighteen for information on working as a careers adviser.)

In some areas there are two levels (or 'tiers') of local government - county councils and district councils, and in other areas there are unitary (i.e. single tier) authorities. County councils provide the large-scale strategic services such as education and highways. Unitary authorities provide all local government services.

As you'll realise from looking at the list of services above, there's a huge range of career opportunities available. A number of these are professional careers. Many careers, such as accountancy and finance, archive work, IT, librarianship, museum work and public relations can be followed both inside and outside local government. For other career areas, such as the police, local government is the major or only employer.

Local government also employs many people in administrative roles, for example managers who hold senior departmental posts. They provide support to council committees and subcommittees, advise councillors, and research and prepare reports, sometimes involving the compilation and analysis of statistical information.

Entry qualifications

Specific entry qualifications vary depending on the position. Some may seek graduates from any discipline, while others of a more specialist nature require or prefer graduates with particular degree subjects.

For the National Graduate Development Programme (see below) you will need a 2:1 degree, in any discipline. The skills sought include the ability to work with others, good communication and persuasion skills, and planning and organisational skills.

Training and career development

Local authorities generally have a good reputation regarding their commitment to the training and development of their staff. Employees often study part time for work-related qualifications, including relevant professional qualifications.

The **National Graduate Development Programme**, run by the Improvement and Development Agency, is a fast-track route for graduates to train and prepare for senior management. It lasts for two years, and is based around a series of core placements within a host local council, supported by an external mentor and the Graduate Leadership Academy. The programme includes skills training and leads to a postgraduate diploma in local government management. You can find out more on: www.ngdp.co.uk.

Some councils run their own graduate training schemes. You can get information on these from their human resources departments. Schemes may be in particular occupational areas, such as finance, or may offer general management training.

Promotion opportunities at senior level may be restricted within a single authority. Career advancement is commonly made by moving from one local authority to another.

Finding vacancies

You can search current vacancies at the official local government jobs website www.LGjobs.com. Otherwise, you should look out for advertisements for specific vacancies. You will find these in *Opportunities: The Public Sector Recruitment Weekly* – see the website at www. opportunities.co.uk. You can also look in relevant professional and trade journals, and in national and local papers.

Recruitment into the National Graduate Development programme, which recruits 80 trainees each year, is through www.ngdp.co.uk.

While at university, or if a recent graduate, you can access current graduate vacancies through your university careers service. Further details about the advice and information available through university careers services are provided in Chapter three.

Sources of further information

www.LGtalent.com – carries information on the range of career opportunities within local government.

The European institutions

The European Commission and other institutions of the European Union (EU) are having an ever-increasing impact on life in the UK and other member countries.

The main European institutions are:

- **The European Commission** – develops legislation; ensures legislation is implemented; represents the community internationally

- **The Council of the European Union** – composed of ministers from each member state; the EU's main decision-making and coordinating body

- **The European Parliament** – approves or amends proposed legislation; has the last word on aspects of the budget

- **The European Court of Justice** – rules on the interpretation and application of EU law

- **The European Court of Auditors** – supervises the EU's budget

- **The European Ombudsman** – deals with complaints against EU institutions and bodies

- The **European Economic and Social Committee** and the **Committee of the Regions** – represent employers and employees, and local and regional bodies.

The European Commission is the largest institution, offering the most employment opportunities. Staff help formulate legislation, develop policies and oversee their day-to-day implementation. Graduates are generally recruited into administrator (AD) grades.

Administrators work in many areas including administration, law, finance, economics, communication and science. Day-to-day work may involve formulating legislation, developing and implementing policies, analysing and advising, coordinating economic and other policies, taking part in trade negotiations, or representing their institution in international meetings. An area of administration that may be of interest to science graduates is responsibility for developing or managing a scientific research programme.

There are some opportunities for scientific research staff, mainly in the European Commission. There are also some research posts in the Directorates-General for Enterprise and Industry, Maritime Affairs and Fisheries, Energy and Transport.

Entry qualifications

You need to be an EU citizen. All staff need to have a very good working knowledge of at least one other official EU language besides their own. People interested in a career in the EU should also have an enthusiasm for working in the EU, strong interpersonal skills and an awareness of current affairs. To be recruited into the AD grades, you need a degree. Some posts may have specific requirements about degree subject and class. Relevant work experience may be required.

You can prepare yourself for working in the EU through applying initially for the European Fast Stream of the UK Civil Service, as described earlier in this chapter. Apart from at least a second class degree, you must have A level French or German at grades A*-C, or equivalent. For the first two years, you will be given EU-related postings in the Civil Service, receive further language training and undertake a six-month work placement in the European Commission. You will then be expected to enter all the EU competitions (the recruitment process for EU vacancies) for which you are eligible.

Training and career development

Further language training is available to those who are appointed. There is a well-defined career structure. The AD grade consists of levels 5 to 16. New entrants start at level 5, and good performance leads to promotion to a higher level. Most people spend three to six years at each level.

Finding vacancies

Recruitment is undertaken by a system called 'open competition'. There are several stages to the recruitment process, taking several months. While each institution is responsible for its own recruitment, joint recruitment competitions are held.

Competitions are advertised in the national press and the Official Journal of the European Union (available online). There's also a centralised recruitment website for all EU institutions, which is operated by the European Personnel Selection Office (EPSO) - listed below.

For information about recruitment for research staff used by the European Commission, see: http://ec.europa.eu/civil_service/job/research_en.htm.

Sources of further information

The European Commission Representation in the UK - tel: 020 7973 1992. www.ec.europa.eu/unitedkingdom

European Personnel Selection Office (EPSO) - Office C-80 00/40, B-1049 Brussels, Belgium. The centralised recruitment website for all EU institutions is: www.europa.eu/epso. (For information on traineeships, having selected the English option, click on 'Discover EU careers' then 'EU careers' and finally 'staff categories'.)

UK Office of the European Parliament - tel: 020 7227 4300. www.europarl.org.uk

Chapter seventeen

Careers in the uniformed services

The main uniformed professions that recruit graduates are the:

- Armed Forces (the Army, Royal Air Force, Royal Navy and Royal Marines)
- police
- prison service.

Although they cover a range of very different activities, they have some things in common:

- they provide a public service, often in dangerous or distressing situations

- there's a lot of discipline – obeying orders is a fundamental aspect of the work, but self-discipline is also important

- they may be in a position of authority over others

- they work unsocial hours.

The nature of the work, the shared risks, the discipline and the irregular hours tend to give the uniformed services a distinct identity and a strong sense of camaraderie.

Armed Forces officer

The main purpose of the Armed Forces is to defend our country – the world is rarely free from conflict and there are constant threats from terrorism, but their work also extends to peacekeeping missions and disaster relief. Servicemen and women must be prepared to risk their lives at any time, whatever the scenario. As well as considering whether you are prepared to take this risk, you also need to face the moral question – would you be prepared to kill or order the killing of others?

If you decide the way of life, and all that it entails, is for you, the Armed Forces offer a huge range of career opportunities. Most officers in the Armed Forces have two roles: to lead and manage a team of people, and to be a technical specialist. The balance between the two roles varies by rank and by the service you're in. It is not necessary to be a graduate to become an officer in the Armed Forces; however, some roles may only be open to graduates of specialist degrees, for example as a dentist, doctor or electronic engineer. Equally, there are also plenty of officer positions for graduates of any discipline.

Each of the Armed Forces operates along broadly similar lines, with personnel typically specialising in one of the following areas:

- **combat** – for example, as officers of the infantry, artillery and armoured regiments of the Army; as warfare officers in the Royal Navy, who command ships and submarines; as pilots and weapon systems officers of the Royal Air Force (RAF) who fly fast jets and helicopters; and as commando officers in the Royal Marines

- **operational support** – the Army Air Corp, for example, carries troops to where they are needed, performs reconnaissance missions and provides airborne command posts; while the

Royal Navy and RAF also offer support roles, such as air traffic controllers and aerospace battle managers

- **engineering** – military engineering during combat operations may include mine clearing, the demolition of key targets with explosives, and post-conflict reconstruction and humanitarian support; on an ongoing basis, engineers maintain, fit and test the full range of military equipment from ships' engines to rocket launchers

- **logistics** – officers working in logistics ensure that the necessary people, equipment and supplies are where they are needed at any given time – at home or on operations

- **intelligence** – involves the collection, analysis and presentation of information about the enemy and aims to combat espionage, subversion and sabotage

- **medical services** – whether in field hospitals or at home, Armed Forces personnel (and animals) need access to healthcare specialists, such as doctors, nurses, dentists, vets etc

- **signals/communications** – involves the maintenance and operation of the various command, control and information systems, as well as providing secure communication worldwide

- **administrative support** – a huge amount of administration is required to run organisations the size and complexity of the Armed Forces; opportunities exist in education and training services, personnel management, public relations, accountancy, legal services, estate management and so on.

Entry qualifications

In general, any degree subject is accepted – although, certainly for some roles, a science or technology degree is an asset, as are language skills. As well as your degree, personal qualities are important. Armed Forces recruiters look for applicants who are assertive and good problem solvers and who have plenty of common sense and initiative. The ability to make quick decisions based on sound judgement is important, as is the ability to express yourself easily and clearly. Obviously, you need to be physically fit and have plenty of stamina, and, perhaps most crucially as an officer, you need leadership skills and the ability to motivate others by your personal example.

Officer recruitment takes place via selection boards. These combine interviews, tests and leadership tasks; these assessment sessions last several days. Procedures vary a little from service to service, but are always rigorous and demanding. The individual boards are:

- the Army Officer Selection Board – for the Army
- the Admiralty Interview Board – for the Royal Navy
- the Officers and Aircrew Selection Centre – for the RAF.

Training and career development

For any of the Armed Forces, initial officer training aims to develop your leadership skills, your understanding of the military and the specialist skills required for your particular role. It is designed to be challenging both physically and mentally, and requires your total commitment. Initial training typically lasts between six to twelve months; however, training will be ongoing throughout your career as required. You will learn a range of skills that are directly transferable to a management career in civilian life. Employers generally welcome people with service experience because of their self-discipline and leadership qualities.

On joining the Armed Forces you will be required to sign up to a minimum period of engagement, the shortest period is around three to four years, although it may be longer where lengthy training is involved. Promotion is usually automatic in the early stages. Promotion to the very highest ranks, though, is by competition and is awarded on merit.

Finding vacancies

Your local Armed Forces Careers Office (AFCO) can give you detailed information about specific jobs, how to apply, the terms of your commission and so on. They also arrange interviews and tests.

If you are still at school you should contact the AFCO to find out more about the scholarships and bursaries available to students during their last two years (aged 16 to 18) at school or college. There are also schemes to sponsor those who wish to become officers through their university course. You should apply as soon as you have a confirmed university place or as soon as possible on starting your degree course.

While at university, or as a recent graduate, you can access information about graduate opportunities in the Armed Forces through your university careers service. Further information about the services available through university careers services is provided in Chapter three.

Sources of further information

You can get more details and copies of up-to-date literature on graduate careers from your local AFCO.

Army careers – tel: 0845 7300111. www.army.mod.uk

RAF careers – tel: 0845 605 555. www.raf.mod.uk/careers

Royal Navy and Royal Marines careers – tel: 0845 600 1444. www.royalnavy.mod.uk and www.royalnavy.mod.uk/marines

Police officer

The UK does not have a national police force, but 43 separate forces in England and Wales, eight in Scotland and one in Northern Ireland. Their role is to protect life and property, and to enforce law and order. When a crime has been committed, police officers provide help to the victims and witnesses, while using a range of traditional and highly sophisticated methods of investigation to identify and apprehend offenders.

All entrants start work as uniformed constables on the beat. The work includes helping members of the public and answering queries, checking the security of premises, apprehending and interviewing suspects, investigating crimes and taking statements from witnesses, and dealing with accidents, disturbances and traffic problems. Not all their time is spent on foot or car patrol. There's a lot of paperwork and some time is spent in court.

Later, you can specialise in areas such as:

- the CID (Criminal Investigation Department), which investigates serious crimes

- the traffic department, which promotes road safety, controls traffic flow, and deals with traffic accidents and offences

- the river police service, which patrols rivers and coastal waters to prevent theft and smuggling, and performs life saving

- a firearms unit, an option for experienced officers who need to pass rigorous and frequent training courses to work as police marksmen.

Entry qualifications

You need to be physically fit and in good health; there are also minimum eyesight standards that apply. Candidates must pass background and security checks, among other criteria regarding eligibility. As a graduate, you could consider the High Potential Development Scheme (HPDS) as a fast-track route to senior leadership positions within the police. Although the scheme is also open to non-graduates, it involves a high level of academic study and a workplace-related dissertation, leading to a postgraduate diploma in police leadership. The highest performers can ultimately undertake a development programme leading to a masters qualification.

The HPDS selection procedure has several stages and includes ability tests, interviews, individual aptitude tests and group exercises. To be accepted onto the HPDS, you need to demonstrate a range of skills in the areas of communication, problem solving, planning and organisation, community focus, respect for race and diversity, strategic thinking and openness to change.

Training and career development

All new recruits undergo a two-year training period called the Initial Police Learning and Development Programme (IPLDP). The training is designed to give student police officers the skills, knowledge and understanding that they will need to do their jobs effectively. The programmes involves on-the-job and classroom-based learning about the community you serve, your local force and its procedures, health and safety, the law, crime prevention and so on. You will undertake placements with different departments within your force, before starting patrol work.

Promotion is through the ranks, from constable through to sergeant, then inspector – at which level your time is divided between operational and management duties. At any rank, you can apply for transfer to another force, and experience in other forces is essential for the more senior postings. The more senior you become, the more you will be involved in liaising with the leaders of the community you serve. Unlike other police officers, those on the HPDS do not have to wait for a vacancy to become available in order to apply for a promotion. Instead they may be promoted by their chief officer as soon as they demonstrate their suitability for the next rank.

Finding vacancies

Vacancies are advertised on the 'Police Could You?' website, listed below. You can only apply for the HPDS after being recruited as a police officer.

Some people work first as special constables or police community support officers as a way of gaining experience, before applying to become a police officer.

While at university, or as a recent graduate, you can access information about vacancies with the police through your university careers service. Further information about the help available through university careers services is provided in Chapter three.

Sources of further information

The National Policing Improvement Agency – tel: 020 7021 7070 (for general enquiries about the HPDS). www.npia.police.uk/hpds

www.policecouldyou.co.uk – for information about the work of the police, plus a list of UK police forces (except Scotland) and their vacancies.

Prison officer

HM Prison Service is entrusted with protecting the public by holding prisoners securely and reducing the risk of them re-offending. In doing so, it aims to care for prisoners in safe and well-ordered establishments; there are about 130 institutions in England and Wales. As well as convicted offenders of all ages who have been sentenced to various terms of imprisonment, there are also remand prisoners awaiting either trial or sentencing by the courts.

The main duty of prison officers is to maintain security and control within a prison: supervising the prisoners in all areas, including during exercise and free time, mealtimes and while they are in their cells. They also receive new prisoners and complete the necessary paperwork. They pass on to senior staff any requests that prisoners may have.

A major role for prison officers is the rehabilitation of convicted offenders. They have daily contact with the prisoners and get to know them well. Officers make sure that individuals get professional help when they need it, and generally prepare them for making the right choices in life outside the prison. For this aspect of their work, prison officers need well-developed communication skills – in order to listen to, influence and help offenders. The ability to form relationships with a diverse range of people is important – some prisoners can be extremely difficult and potentially violent, while others are at risk from suicide or self-harm.

Entry qualifications

For general entry to the service there are no specific academic requirements, but the National Offender Management Scheme (NOMS) offers a programme aimed exclusively at graduates who are either predicted, or who have gained, a 2:1 degree in any subject. The selection process includes ability tests, role-play exercises, written tests and an interview.

Applicants to the scheme need to believe in the value of rehabilitation and be able to demonstrate the skills needed to eventually take on senior leadership roles within the prison service. For example, you need to be decisive – yet fair and calm, even in volatile situations. Self-confidence is also important – you can't be intimidated by individuals or events, and if you do face problems, you need the resilience to persevere.

The Prison Service also directly recruits into a wide range of functions suitable for graduates, including forensic psychology, finance, procurement, human resources and healthcare.

Training and career development

The NOMS Graduate Programme lasts three years and begins with a six-week course at the national training centre in Rugby. Here you learn the basic duties of a prison officer, such as applying control and restraint techniques, using handcuffs and conducting searches. The final week of the course is spent shadowing a prison officer at work, after which you will be given your first post. By the third year of the programme, you will be expected to take on managerial responsibilities – perhaps as an operational manager or on a secondment with the Ministry of Justice. At the end of the graduate programme, you will need to gain a broad range of experience (of different risk categories; of male, female and juvenile prisoners; and of the different functions of the prison service) before you can take on a position as a deputy governor or governor of your own prison.

Finding vacancies

Recruitment drives for the NOMS Graduate Programme operate on an annual basis; full details are available on the HM Prison Service website listed below. Check with HM Prison Service for the deadline for applications, or sign up for 'job alerts' via their website.

While at university, or as a recent graduate, you can access information about graduate vacancies available with HM Prison Service through your university careers service. Further information about the help available through university careers services is provided in Chapter three.

Sources of further information

HM Prison Service – tel: 020 7217 600. www.hmprisonservice.gov.uk

Chapter eighteen

Other options

It would be impossible to list all possible careers that are open to you – if you refer back to Chapter five, you will see that graduate destinations are many and varied! With some research, and perhaps some advice and guidance from a professional careers adviser, you may be able to identify many more careers that would suit your situation.

This chapter covers just a few more options you may like to consider, in the areas of:

- careers guidance
- housing
- ICT
- legal work
- retailing.

Finally, you might like to give a thought to self-employment, which, if you have a commercially-viable idea and the skills to deliver it, can be a tempting proposition! Information about self-employment is provided at the end of this chapter.

Careers guidance

Careers guidance specialists, or careers advisers, help people of all ages make decisions about their education, training and future career. Their role is not to tell people what to do, but instead to help their clients come to a better understanding of their options and help them plan how to achieve their goals, based on their individual abilities, preferences and priorities.

The work involves one-to-one interviews with clients; group sessions; advising other professionals, such as teachers; report writing and record keeping. Careers advisers may help organise careers events in association with employers, training providers and educational institutions – and must keep up to date with local and national issues relating to careers. In some settings the work may involve liaising with potential employers and helping people find work or work experience.

Careers advisers may be employed within the government-funded Connexions and nextstep services (in England) or in Careers Services (in Wales, Scotland and Northern Ireland). They may also be directly employed by schools, colleges and universities. Other employers include private agencies and, occasionally, professional organisations, major employers and voluntary organisations.

N.B. There are plans to replace the nextstep service with a new 'adult advancement and careers service' in England, during 2010.

Entry qualifications

Specific entry requirements vary, but the most widely accepted professional careers qualification is the Qualification in Careers Guidance (QCG), which takes one year, full time, or two years, part time. It is open to graduates of any subject, and involves postgraduate-level study at a university combined with work-based learning. Alternatively, there are masters degrees in careers guidance and related subjects. It is also possible to qualify if you are already in relevant employment and have gained experience of working in guidance, by undertaking training leading to the NVQ level 4 in advice and guidance.

You need to have a real interest in people and be able to establish relationships quickly. Communication and listening skills are vital and you must be non-judgemental and patient. You will also need to be effective in using a wide range of paper-based and computerised information sources.

Training and career development

Advisers wishing to work in the Connexions service must complete additional training leading to specific units of the NVQ level 4 in learning, development and support services (LDSS) for children, young people and those who care for them. Connexions personal advisers (PAs) not only give guidance on careers, but also on a range of other issues relevant to young people such as housing, benefits, health issues, drugs and relationships.

Careers advisers and PAs undertake continuing professional development (CPD) throughout their careers. It is possible to specialise in working with different client groups, such as young people or adults, people with special needs, people in higher education, etc. With experience there are opportunities to take on supervisory or management positions, or to work on a self-employed basis as a careers consultant.

Finding vacancies

Jobs are advertised in *Portico* – a fortnightly vacancy bulletin published by the Institute of Career Guidance (ICG), in *The Guardian*, *The Independent* and *Times Higher Education*. Both the ICG and the Association of Graduate Careers Advisory Services (AGCAS) list vacancies on their websites.

While at university, or as a recent graduate, you can access information about potential employers and current graduate vacancies through your university careers service. Further information about the help available through university careers services is provided in Chapter three.

Sources of further information

Association of Graduate Careers Advisory Services (AGCAS) – tel: 0114 251 5750. www.agcas.org.uk

Institute of Career Guidance (ICG) – tel: 01384 376464. www.icg-uk.org

Housing

People working in housing are responsible for the planning, construction, allocation and upkeep of rented properties. Many jobs are concerned with creating and maintaining sustainable communities (places where people want to live and work, now and in the future). Graduates with a degree in any subject may find vacancies as a trainee housing manager. You are likely to be given experience of a wide range of responsibilities before, possibly, specialising in one area. You may get involved in planning housing requirements; purchasing land; commissioning new builds; managing lettings, transfers and exchanges; overseeing repairs and maintenance; and working with other agencies to maintain good community relations.

The major employers are housing associations and local government bodies, such as district councils. The role of the local authority housing department is to make sure that the housing needs of their area are met. That includes making land available for building. Increasingly, responsibility for the management and the provision of new housing has moved to housing associations. Large private estates, cooperatives, charities and property-owning companies may also employ housing managers or property managers. The Armed Forces employ housing managers drawn from the ranks of serving officers.

Entry qualifications

You may be competing with people who have degrees in subjects more relevant to this career area; however, jobs are usually available to graduates of any subject and employers may be more concerned about the personal qualities and interests of potential employees. Postgraduate qualifications in subjects such as housing studies or sustainable communities may be useful.

You will need good communication and presentation skills. Commercial awareness and negotiation skills are also important. The work can be pressurised and you may need to develop a thorough understanding of relevant legislation, government policy and building construction.

Training and career development

Once in employment, there are opportunities to take relevant qualifications through part-time study or distance learning, including those offered by the Chartered Institute of Housing (CIH). Many people working in housing become members of the CIH. For information on membership grades and the requirements for each level, contact the CIH or see their website – listed at the end of this section.

Finding vacancies

The weekly magazine, *Inside Housing* (and its associated website) lists job vacancies in social housing. For vacancies within local government, visit www.LGtalent.com. Vacancies are also advertised by recruitment agencies, on many specialist and general online job sites, in the appointments sections of certain daily newspapers (particularly the society section of *The Guardian*, published every Wednesday) and on employers' own websites.

The National Housing Federation publishes a list of around 1,200 housing associations in its *Directory of Members*, which may be useful in finding employers in a particular area. The directory may be available for reference in your local library, or visit www.nhfdirectory.co.uk.

While at university, or as a recent graduate, you can access information about potential employers and current graduate vacancies through your university careers service. Further information about the help available through university careers services is provided in Chapter three.

Sources of further information

Asset Skills - the Sector Skills Council covering the housing sector. Tel: 0800 056 7160. www.assetskills.org

Chartered Institute of Housing (CIH) - tel: 024 7685 1700. www.cih.org

Institute of Residential Property Management - tel: 020 7622 5092. www.irpm.org.uk

National Housing Federation - tel: 020 7067 1010. www.housing.org.uk and www.nhfdirectory.co.uk

ICT

Computers are used in every type of workplace you can think of and, while you need a relevant degree to work in the more technical roles, there are many opportunities that are open to graduates of any discipline.

For example, **systems analysts and designers** first investigate and analyse a business problem, such as introducing a new booking system for hospital appointments or a complex payroll system, before identifying, costing and assessing potential ICT solutions. The work also involves project management - overseeing budgets, schedules and the work involved in implementing the new system.

Software may need to be developed or adapted to meet the business requirements and this is where people with programming skills come in. **Software developers** may specialise in different types of programming, such as website or back-end development. The work involves specifying what functionality the programme needs before writing and testing the code.

Database managers take responsibility for maintaining and developing an organisation's databases, which may store information about customers, accounts, orders, stock levels, etc. **ICT or systems managers** may have overall responsibility for the way ICT is used within an organisation, setting its policies and developing its long-term vision.

Entry qualifications

You may be competing with people who have degrees in subjects more relevant to this career area; however employers often use aptitude tests to assess an applicant's suitability, and then provide specialist training. Postgraduate conversion courses in computing and ICT are available for graduates with unrelated degrees.

You need a logical mind as well as analytical and problem-solving skills for this type of work. The ability to work well in a team and communicate complex ideas to non-specialists is also important.

Training and career development

Training may be in-house or you may be able to work towards professional qualifications through part-time study or distance learning. Relevant qualifications are offered by the BCS (The Chartered Institute for IT), the Institute for the Management of Information Systems and some larger computer companies, such as Microsoft.

Finding vacancies

Vacancies are advertised by specialist recruitment agencies, on many specialist and general online job sites, in the appointments sections of certain daily newspapers and on employers' own websites.

While at university, or as a recent graduate, you can access information about potential employers and current graduate vacancies through your university careers service. Further information about the help available through university careers services is provided in Chapter three.

Sources of further information

BCS: The Chartered Institute for IT - tel: 0845 300 4417. www.bcs.org

e-skills UK - the Sector Skills Council for business and information technology. www.e-skills.com

Institute for the Management of Information Systems - tel: 0700 00 23456. www.imis.org.uk

Institution of Analysts and Programmers – tel: 020 8567 2118. www.iap.org.uk

The Institution of Engineering and Technology (IET) – tel: 01438 313311. www.theiet.org

Women in Technology – an organisation that aims to increase the number of women working as IT professionals, and to help them build successful careers. www.womenintechnology.co.uk

Legal work

Barristers work in the courts defending and prosecuting cases referred to them by solicitors. They may also represent clients at public enquiries. Some barristers work as legal advisers and consultants. Queen's Counsels (QCs) and judges are selected from the ranks of barristers. Most barristers are self-employed, and work in chambers (offices). There are also employed opportunities, working for the Crown Prosecution Service and in the Government Legal Service.

Solicitors have day-to-day contact with the public, giving advice on all kinds of legal matters. They represent clients in the county courts and magistrates' courts (and, in certain circumstances, in the higher courts). Solicitors give instructions to barristers for the cases that barristers present in court. Solicitors usually specialise in areas such as property sale and purchase, company law, family law or criminal law. Solicitors work in private practice, commerce and industry and for local government and the Civil Service, including the Crown Prosecution Service and the Government Legal Service.

Entry qualifications

Graduates of any subject can train to become barristers or solicitors. You need at least a second-class honours degree for entry to a conversion course; some employers may require at least a 2:1.

In addition, you also need a high level of intellect and ability to take in and assess large amounts of information. Self confidence is required along with well-developed presentation and communication skills. You will need to be able to relate to a wide range of people and have the mental and physical stamina to deal with often long and complex cases.

Training and career development

To become a barrister or solicitor, non-law graduates must take a one-year, full-time (or two-year, part-time) conversion course – either the Common Professional Examination or an approved Graduate Diploma in Law.

Would-be barristers follow this by taking the Bar Professional Training Course (BPTC) – one year, full time or two years, part time. From September 2010, nine institutions will offer BPTCs; course fees cost around £14,000, although a limited number of grants and scholarships are available. During the BPTC, you develop practical skills in, for example, casework, negotiation and research. The next stage is to undertake a year's pupillage with an experienced barrister. After that, you apply for a tenancy in a set of chambers or for an employed position. Competition is stiff at all stages of the training.

To train as a solicitor, non-law graduates must take a conversion course, as described above. This must be followed by the Legal Practice Course (one year, full time or two years, part time – some more flexible routes are also available) and finally, you must find a two-year training contract in a solicitor's office or other approved organisation, during which you take a professional skills course. There is a great deal of competition for training contract positions.

Finding vacancies

Useful information about how to take your first steps into law can be found on www.lawcareers.net – published in association with the Law Society.

Sources of further information

The Bar Council – tel: 020 7242 0082. www.barcouncil.org.uk

Bar Standards Board – tel: 020 7611 1444. www.barstandardsboard.org.uk

Government Legal Service – tel: 0845 3000 793. www.gls.gov.uk

The Law Society – tel: 020 7242 1222. www.lawsociety.org.uk

Solicitors Regulation Authority – tel: 0870 606 2555. www.sra.org.uk

www.lawcareers.net – provides information about careers and training, as well as advertising vacancies for training posts and permanent positions.

Retailing

Large retailers offer many graduate opportunities in a variety of jobs such as finance, quality assurance, marketing, buying, merchandising and IT. Some of these functions are described in Chapter fifteen. However, the majority of openings are in **store management**.

Most vacancies are in supermarkets, multiples (chain stores specialising in areas such as electrical goods, books, outdoor sports, furniture and fashion) and department stores. Retail management may involve being in charge of a department – being responsible for staff, meeting sales targets, merchandising, dealing with customer complaints, health and safety, and security; or working as a branch manager – with similar responsibilities, but also involved in recruitment and training, organising sales promotions, stock control and so on.

Depending on the type of store you work for, you may be expected to work shifts; for example, some supermarkets are open 24 hours a day.

Entry qualifications

Graduate management training schemes usually accept any degree subject. It can be useful to be able to demonstrate relevant work experience and a good knowledge of the particular company that you wish to work for.

Training and career development

Training programmes tend to combine formal training with experience in different sections of the business, e.g. finance, HR and merchandising. This may involve travelling to, or working in, other parts of the country.

Finding vacancies

Vacancies are advertised on the websites of the major retailers and on many specialist and general online job sites. A useful website for vacancies, which includes a section for graduates, can be found at www.inretail.co.uk.

While at university, or as a recent graduate, you can access information about potential employers and current graduate vacancies through your university careers service. Further information about the help available through university careers services is provided in Chapter three.

Sources of further information

Skillsmart Retail - the Sector Skills Council for the retail industry. Tel: 020 7462 5060. www.skillsmartretail.com

Self-employment

Almost four million people in the UK are self-employed, a figure that includes people who run their own businesses in the usual sense, as well as those who work freelance for different employers. Opportunities for self-employment vary considerably, depending on your knowledge, skills and interests.

Graduates who have qualified in a profession such as law, accountancy, dentistry and so on, can consider becoming self-employed and running their own practice. Others with management skills, for example, could potentially work as consultants or interim managers (for example, covering for the long-term absence of another manager). If you are enterprising and wish to go into business, then it will be down to you to research your market, devise a business plan and seek any necessary finance. Franchise opportunities allow you to buy into an established brand, although can still require large amounts of investment capital.

Entry qualifications

The most important requirements for self-employment relate to your personal drive, ambition and commercial awareness. You will need motivation and determination to succeed, and confidence and flexibility to do a wide range of tasks in support of your business. Skills in planning and organisation are critical. You will also need a good understanding of the rules and regulations that apply to your type of business - including VAT, insurance, health and safety, data protection, etc.

Training and career development

You could consider taking courses in business, marketing, bookkeeping, IT and management. Many such courses are available on a distance-learning or part-time basis. There are several different agencies and organisations that offer advice, workshops, networking opportunities, mentoring, and so on to people who are considering self-employment; see below for further details.

Finding opportunities

While at university, or as a recent graduate, you should be able to access information about self-employment through your university careers service. Further information about the help available through university careers services is provided in Chapter three.

Sources of further information

British Franchise Association – tel: 01865 379892. www.thebfa.org

Business Link – a service operating across England, supported by government departments, agencies and local authorities, which advises new small- and medium-size businesses. Tel: 0845 600 9 006. www.businesslink.gov.uk

Co-operatives UK – tel: 0161 246 2900. www.cooperatives-uk.coop

Enterprise UK – an organisation run in partnership between the Department for Business, Innovation and Skills; British Chamber of Commerce; Confederation of British Industry; Federation of Small Businesses; and Institute of Directors. Tel: 020 7430 8010. www.enterpriseuk.org

Federation of Small Businesses – tel: 01253 336000. www.fsb.org.uk

Flexible Support for Business – a service provided by the Welsh Assembly Government that offers support and advice for businesses in Wales. Tel: 0300 060 3000. http://fs4b.wales.gov.uk

www.hmrc.gov.uk/selfemployed – HM Revenue & Customs.

www.shell-livewire.org – offers free online advice and support for anyone who is considering starting a business.

www.venturenavigator.co.uk – an online service, funded by the Government and created by a consortium of seven universities, that allows people with a business start-up idea to assess the viability of their idea, access relevant guidance and network with others.

Section 4
Other sources of information and advice

Chapter nineteen

Other sources of information and advice

This chapter lists some of the main organisations, websites and careers resources that may be useful to you.

Societies, institutes and professional bodies

Science Council – an organisation representing various learned and professional bodies. Promotes the profession of scientist through the award of chartered scientist (CSci) status. Tel: 020 7922 7888. www.sciencecouncil.org and www.charteredscientist.org

Engineering Council – tel: 020 3206 0500. www.engc.org.uk

EngineeringUK – tel: 020 3206 0400. www.engineeringuk.com

IET (The Institution of Engineering and Technology) – tel: 01438 313311. www.theiet.org

Institute of Physics – tel: 020 7470 4800. www.iop.org

The Institute of Science & Technology – tel: 0114 276 3197. www.istonline.org.uk

The Royal Society – the national academy of science in the UK and the Commonwealth. Tel: 020 7451 2500. http://royalsociety.org

Royal Society of Chemistry (RSC) – tel: 020 7437 8656. www.rsc.org

Society of Biology – tel: 020 7936 5900. www.societyofbiology.org

Women's Engineering Society (WES) – a society for students on engineering and related courses, as well as people working in the fields of engineering, science and technology. Tel: 01438 765506. www.wes.org.uk

Organisations and websites that promote scientific and related careers

British Science Association – organises initiatives across the UK to inspire people to engage with science. Tel: 0870 770 7101. www.britishscienceassociation.org

EDT – a charity that runs schemes aimed at inspiring young people to choose a career in science, technology, engineering or mathematics. Tel: 01707 81520. www.etrust.org.uk

The Smallpeice Trust – a charity that runs programmes promoting engineering careers to young people. Tel: 01926 333200. www.smallpeicetrust.org.uk

WISE (Women into Science, Engineering and Construction) – a campaign run in collaboration with partners in industry and education that aims to encourage girls to pursue courses and careers in science, technology, engineering, mathematics and construction. Tel: 020 3206 0408. www.wisecampaign.org.uk

www.enginuity.org.uk – provides information about engineering and technology careers.

www.futuremorph.org – an initiative lead by the Science Council to promote careers in science, technology, engineering and mathematics.

www.scenta.co.uk – provides information about engineering and technology careers.

http://sciencesowhat.direct.gov.uk – a Government-backed website that aims to stimulate interest in science and offer opportunities to get involved. Also has a section on careers information.

www.stemnet.org.uk – aims to increase young people's choice and chances through science, technology, engineering and mathematics. Tel: 020 3206 0450.

Research Councils

Research Council UK – www.rcuk.ac.uk

Biotechnology and Biological Sciences Research Council (BBSRC) – tel: 01793 413200. www.bbsrc.ac.uk

Engineering and Physical Sciences Research Council (EPSRC) – tel: 01793 444100. www.epsrc.ac.uk

Medical Research Council (MRC) - tel: 020 7636 5422.
www.mrc.ac.uk

Natural Environment Research Council (NERC) - tel: 01793 411500.
www.nerc.ac.uk

Science and Technology Facilities Council (STFC) - tel: 01793
442000. www.stfc.ac.uk

Sector Skills Councils

Sector Skills Councils (SSCs) are independent, employer-led
organisations that represent the issues relating to the skills of the
UK's workforce. SSCs provide information about relevant training and
qualifications for careers in their sector. The SSCs that are relevant to
the careers listed in this book are given below.

Asset Skills - covers the housing sector. Tel: 0800 056 7160.
www.assetskills.org

Cogent - covers the chemicals, pharmaceuticals, and polymers
industries. Tel: 01925 515200. www.cogent-careers.com

Creative & Cultural Skills - covers the crafts, cultural heritage,
design, literature, music, performing arts and visual arts sectors.
Tel: 020 7015 1800. www.ccskills.org.uk and www.creative-choices.co.uk

Energy & Utility Skills - covers the gas, power, waste management
and water industries. Tel: 0845 077 9922. www.euskills.co.uk/careers

e-skills UK - covers business and information technology.
www.e-skills.com

Financial Services Skills Council - covers financial services,
accountancy and finance. Tel: 0845 257 3772. www.fssc.org.uk

Improve Ltd - covers the food and drink industry. Tel: 0845 644 0448.
www.improveltd.co.uk and www.improve-skills.co.uk

Lantra - covers the environmental and land-based sector. Tel: 0845
707 8007. www.lantra.co.uk and www.afuturein.com

Lifelong Learning UK (LLUK) - covers careers in careers guidance,
further education, higher education, libraries, archives and information
services. Tel: 0300 303 1877. www.lluk.org

Semta - covers science, engineering and manufacturing technologies.
Tel: 0800 282 167 (learning helpline). www.semta.org.uk

Skills for Justice – covers the justice sector. Tel: 0114 261 1499. www.skillsforjustice.com

SkillsActive – covers the active leisure and learning sector. Tel: 08000 933300 (careers advice line). www.skillsactive.com/careers

Skillset – covers the advertising and creative media sector. Tel: 08080 300 900 (in England and N.Ireland) or 0800 012 1815 (in Wales). www.skillset.org/careers

Skillsmart Retail – covers the retail industry. Tel: 020 7462 5060. www.skillsmartretail.com

Other useful resources and websites

The *Student Helpbook Series*, published by Lifetime Publishing, is designed to help students of all ages make the right choice about their careers and education. Relevant titles in this series include:

Careers with an Arts or Humanities Degree (the companion guide to this book), £12.99
Decisions at 15/16+, £12.99
Decisions at 17/18+, £11.99
Student Life: a Survival Guide, £11.99

Lifetime Publishing also publishes a guide to choosing your A levels, Advanced Diplomas and other post-16 qualifications:
Which A Levels? £14.99

Books in the *UCAS Progression Series* cover topics such as an introduction to the subject area, career options, entry routes and entry requirements and are priced at £15.99 each. Relevant titles in this series are:

Progression to Engineering and Mathematics
Progression to Health and Social Care
Progression to Medicine, Dentistry and Optometry
Progression to Sports Science and Physiotherapy

The *Careers Uncovered* series, published by Trotman, looks at a range of professional careers and gives facts, such as potential salary and working conditions, and advice on how to get into each industry. Relevant titles are:

Careers Uncovered: Medicine, £12.99

Careers Uncovered: Nursing & Midwifery, £14.99

Careers Uncovered: Engineering, £9.99

www.civilservice.gov.uk/jobs – for vacancies across all government departments.

www.LGtalent.com – carries information on the range of career opportunities within local government.

www.naturejobs.com – a website that advertises vacancies for science jobs, operated in association with the journal *Nature*.

www.newscientistjobs.com – a website that advertises vacancies for science jobs, studentships and courses, operated in association with the journal *New Scientist*.

www.nhscareers.nhs.uk – provides information about a wide range of medical and health-related careers.

www.prospects.ac.uk – the graduate careers website. Provides a searchable directory of postgraduate courses, as well as listing graduate vacancies and work experience opportunities. Also provides information on graduate careers.

www.ucas.com – the Universities and Colleges Admissions Service. Manages applications to higher education (HE) and provides a searchable directory of HE courses.

Index

More titles in the Student Helpbook series ...

helping students of all ages make the right choices about their careers and education.

Careers with an Arts or Humanities Degree – Over 100 job ideas to inspire you

An excellent read for anyone considering arts or humanities subjects at degree level.

5ᵗʰ edition £12.99   ISBN: 978-1-904979-40-1

Which A levels? – The guide to choosing A levels, Advanced Diplomas and other post-16 qualifications

The highly popular, student-friendly guide. Features over 50 A level subjects and the range of Advanced Diplomas. Includes career options after A levels/Advanced Diplomas and as a graduate.

7ᵗʰ edition £14.99   ISBN: 978-1-904979-41-8

Jobs and Careers after A levels and equivalent advanced qualifications

Opportunities for students leaving school or college at 18, including advice on job-hunting, applications and interviews.

9ᵗʰ edition £11.99   ISBN: 978-1-904979-21-0

CVs and Applications

For anyone who is applying for a job or college place; includes details of how to use the internet in marketing yourself.

7ᵗʰ edition £12.99   ISBN: 978-1-904979-44-9

Excel at Interviews

This highly successful book makes invaluable reading for students and jobhunters.

6ᵗʰ edition £11.99   ISBN: 978-1-904979-22-7

Visit us online to view our full range of resources at:
www.lifetime-publishing.co.uk